THE AUSTRALIAN Women's Weekly

2-DAY FASTING DIET

TRIPLE TESTED · FOR YOUR SUCCESS EVERY TIME

contents

A history of fasting

The practice of fasting for health or spiritual reasons is as old as the hills. Pretty much every religion, and many Eastern philosophies, have forms of fasting. Typically fasting is promoted as a means of discipline and for focusing the mind. More recently, fasting has been promoted as a means to weight loss. So, does it work and is it safe?

Until relatively recently, humans had forced periods of fasting due to the availability of food. Cycles of feast and famine would have been common from our days as hunter-gatherers thousands of years ago, right through until less than a century ago. It is only more recently in human history that food has been so plentiful and available to us.

Dr Joanna McMillan
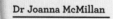

Accredited Practising Dietitian and Nutritionist
www.drjoanna.com.au
www.getlean.com.au

Do we have 'thrifty genes'?

There is no doubt our bodies are built to cope with periods of little or no food. In fact, one theory of why we struggle with our weight today is called the 'thrifty gene hypothesis'. The theory goes that our ancestors – those who wasted little energy and conserved it well by preserving body fat in times of famine – survived to pass on their genes. Today, the 'thrifty' genes that kept our ancestors alive are making us fat because we live in an environment of abundant energy-dense food and do little exercise. So one way of looking at things is that integrating regular fasting into your life is just emanating the environment we evolved to survive in.

Can fasting help us to lose weight and keep it off?

The truth is we don't really know yet. What we certainly know from animal studies is that eating fewer kilojoules lengthens an animal's lifespan and lowers their risk of many chronic diseases, including cancer. There is pretty good evidence that this also occurs in humans. It's just more difficult to test, since getting people to survive on lower kilojoule intakes is not easy.

There is also some evidence that fasting has benefits from a health perspective. For example, studies of people at the end of Ramadan have shown improvements in indicators of heart disease risk, such as blood cholesterol profiles and insulin sensitivity. Whether this translates into long-term reductions in risk is not yet known, but it certainly looks promising. Studies of

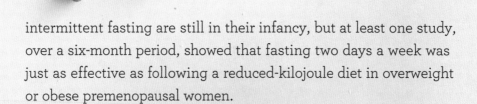

intermittent fasting are still in their infancy, but at least one study, over a six-month period, showed that fasting two days a week was just as effective as following a reduced-kilojoule diet in overweight or obese premenopausal women.

Previous studies have tended to look at longer-term fasting over several days. Most have not shown any good long-term results. It seems that after a few days the body really does kick into starvation mode, hanging on to make the stored energy last as long as possible, and then ramping up the appetite to restore the body's weight once food becomes available. However, this is a small concern and the bottom line is that chronic dieting and regaining weight is likely to be much more harmful. This is very different to intermittent fasting. Most of us are well able to cope with a single day of fasting at a time.

Is there any harm from fasting?

This 2-day fast diet works on a 2100kJ/500-calorie total daily intake for women, and a 2500kJ/600-calorie total daily intake for men. What will certainly not work is if you fast for two days, but on the other days you overeat and more than make up for the spared kilojoules. However, the research on fasting seems to show this doesn't happen to most of us.

You may be more likely to eat a bigger breakfast on the day after your fast, but the evidence to date suggests that most of us only eat about 20 per cent more the next day, and do not therefore replace all the kilojoules omitted on the fast day. But do be mindful of this.

It's also important that you don't 'eat whatever you like' on the other days. Nutrient intake matters! We need micronutrients and phytochemicals such as antioxidants for optimal health. Our food choices affect more than just our weight, it also affects how we look and feel, and our risk of disease.

I do have some concerns over the long term effects of fasting. It may well be that our bodies just learn to cope better with a fast. In other words, we perhaps just get better at preserving energy while fasting, and get better at storing energy as fat both before and after the fast. If that is the case, you would need to continue fasting for evermore, or risk putting some weight on when you stop.

If this were to happen, you'd have to keep up the fasting routine forever just to remain weight stable, but should you stop fasting you risk gaining extra fat ready for the next fast that never comes. We need to wait for further research to understand more about these effects.

Those who should certainly not undertake fasting include pregnant and breast-feeding women, those with diabetes or those who are prone to hypoglycaemia and with any pre-existing medical problems. Many medications must be taken with food, and so you must not fast unless under the guidance of your doctor.

Pros OF FASTING

● You learn to feel properly hungry and be okay with that. This may sound funny, but so many people tell me they are rarely hungry, or they are scared of being hungry. Most of us can easily cope with one day of little food.

● Anecdotally, many people say they feel full of energy post their fast day, and feel quite euphoric. That may be from a sense of pride at their restraint, or there may be physiological reasons. By giving your body a rest from digestion, you feel lighter and have more energy to direct into other things!

● Provided you don't go crazy and overeat on the other days, it can be a terrific means of lowering your weekly kilojoule intake and chipping away at your fat stores.

● You only have to restrict your food intake on two days out of seven. For many people, this is much easier, and a whole lot more appealing, than having to think about a small restriction in food every day.

● You can change the days you fast, so if you have a dinner or celebration on the day you normally fast, you can swap it for the next day.

500-calorie MENU PLANNER

Menu 1

This menu is for those who can last through to lunch by having a drink mid-morning to keep the hunger at bay.

iced mint and green tea
(page 109) 44 cal

tuna carrot and zucchini salad with pitta chips
(page 26) 202 cal

lentil and carrot soup
(page 93) 249 cal

Total calories 495

Menu 2

This menu is for you if you feel the need for a substantial meal three times a day.

soft-boiled egg with prosciutto-wrapped asparagus
(page 10) 88 cal

radish and lentil salad
(page 29) 220 cal

crab and zucchini 'spaghetti'
(page 71) 186 cal

Total calories 494

Menu 3

This menu is for the weekend faster – it would suit someone who is a weekend or shift worker.

cinnamon and pear porridge
(page 21) 99 cal

roasted tomato and cumin soup
(page 52) 178 cal

apricot stuffed pork with rocket, mint and radish salad
(page 98) 213 cal

Total calories 490

Menu 4

This menu is for the snacker, who will eat 6 small meals throughout the day.

choc-honey balls
(page 104) 49 cal

roasted pumpkin seed spiced trail mix
(page 105) 49 cal

cottage cheese and tuna dip
(page 106) 53 cal

strawberry and watermelon juice
(page 108) 50 cal

spiced lamb skewers on fattoush
(page 94) 303 cal

Total calories 504

600-calorie
MENU PLANNER

Menu 1

This is a filling protein power menu.

soft-boiled egg with sumac salt
(page 22) 88 cal

creamy spinach dip
(page 106) 48 cal

pesto turkey couscous salad
(page 58) 209 cal

gazpacho juice
(page 108) 42 cal

beef and mushroom meatloaf
(page 67) 208 cal

Total calories 595

Menu 2

This menu is for those on-the-go.

salmon and dill rice cake
(page 13) 95 cal

poached chicken salad with dijon dressing
(page 36) 211 cal

tomato and zucchini tart
(page 70) 303 cal

Total calories 609

Menu 3

This menu is for vegetarians.

baked beans and ricotta-stuffed mushroom
(page 18) 94 cal

vegie hash with kale, chickpeas and poached egg
(page 30) 205 cal

zucchini and corn fritters
(page 85) 240 cal

coconut pistachio bites
(page 105) 41 cal

Total calories 580

Menu 4

This menu is for the comfort eater.

cinnamon and pear porridge
(page 21) 99 cal

curried vegetable soup
(page 39) 156 cal

spiced pumpkin dip
(page 107) 50 cal

one-pot chicken with soba noodles
(page 82) 288 cal

Total calories 593

breakfast

soft-boiled egg with prosciutto-wrapped asparagus

PREP + COOK TIME 15 MINUTES • SERVES 1

1 small egg (42g)

3 small asparagus spears (50g), trimmed

¼ slice prosciutto (5g), cut lengthways into 3 strips

1 Place egg in a small saucepan, cover with cold water; bring to the boil over high heat. Reduce heat to medium, simmer for 2 minutes; remove egg from pan.

2 Add asparagus to pan; boil for 1 minute or until just tender, drain. Refresh asparagus and egg under cold water; shell egg.

3 Serve egg and asparagus with prosciutto; season to taste.

NUTRITIONAL COUNT PER SERVING

▶ 5.4g total fat
▶ 1.9g saturated fat
▶ 370kJ (88 cal)
▶ 0.6g carbohydrate
▶ 8.8g protein
▶ 0.7g fibre

Test Kitchen
NOTE

For a different take on the recipe, poach the egg and char-grill the asparagus and the prosciutto.

apple and cinnamon cereal

PREP TIME 5 MINUTES • SERVES 1

1 tablespoon (10g) rolled oats

2 tablespoons (10g) All-Bran

2 tablespoons skim milk

¼ medium apple (40g), cut into matchsticks

pinch ground cinnamon

1 Combine oats and bran in a small bowl; top with milk and apple, sprinkle with cinnamon. Serve immediately.

Use the remaining apple for a 20 calorie snack.

salmon and dill rice cake

PREP TIME 5 MINUTES • SERVES 1

1 tablespoon low-fat cottage cheese
½ teaspoon finely chopped fresh dill
½ teaspoon finely grated lemon rind
1 x 7g (¼ ounce) rice cake
35g (1 ounce) smoked salmon slices
½ teaspoon fresh dill, extra

1 Combine cheese, dill and rind in a small bowl. Spread cheese mixture over rice cake.

2 Top rice cake with salmon. Sprinkle with extra dill leaves; season to taste.

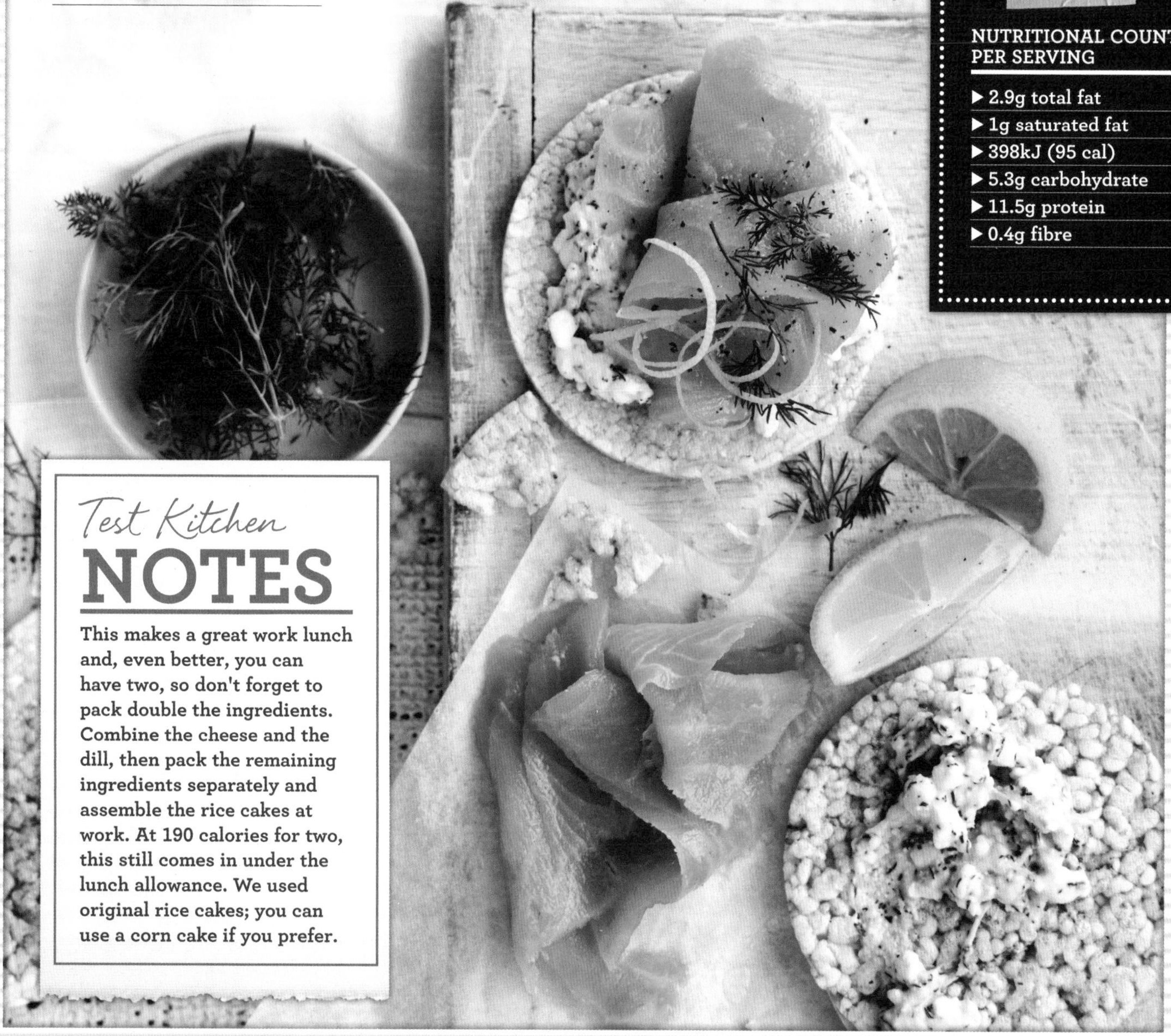

NUTRITIONAL COUNT PER SERVING

- 2.9g total fat
- 1g saturated fat
- 398kJ (95 cal)
- 5.3g carbohydrate
- 11.5g protein
- 0.4g fibre

Test Kitchen
NOTES

This makes a great work lunch and, even better, you can have two, so don't forget to pack double the ingredients. Combine the cheese and the dill, then pack the remaining ingredients separately and assemble the rice cakes at work. At 190 calories for two, this still comes in under the lunch allowance. We used original rice cakes; you can use a corn cake if you prefer.

green smoothie

1 small apple (130g), peeled, cored, chopped coarsely

6 medium baby cos (romaine) lettuce leaves (50g)

25g (¾ ounce) baby spinach leaves

100g (3 ounces) coarsely chopped honeydew melon

¾ cup (180ml) water

crushed ice, to serve, optional

1 Blend or process ingredients until smooth; serve over ice, if you like.

NUTRITIONAL COUNT PER SERVING

▶ 0.4g total fat
▶ 0.1g saturated fat
▶ 408kJ (97 cal)
▶ 19g carbohydrate
▶ 2.2g protein
▶ 4g fibre

Have all ingredients stored in the refrigerator for an extra cold smoothie. The smoothie will separate on standing, so serve immediately, or give it a brisk stir and it will come back together.

berry protein smoothie

½ cup (75g) frozen mixed berries

50g (1½ ounces) silken tofu

1 tablespoon no-fat vanilla yoghurt

2 tablespoons skim milk

2 tablespoons water

crushed ice, to serve

1 Blend ingredients until smooth. Pour into a glass with ice; serve immediately.

Blend with ½ cup ice to make the smoothie thicker.

NUTRITIONAL COUNT PER SERVING

▶ 1.2g total fat
▶ 0.2g saturated fat
▶ 401kJ (96 cal)
▶ 11.3g carbohydrate
▶ 7.4g protein
▶ 3.6g fibre

crumpet with raspberries and cinnamon honey

PREP + COOK TIME 5 MINUTES • SERVES 1

1 crumpet

20g (¾ ounce) fresh raspberries
(about 7 raspberries)

½ teaspoon honey

pinch ground cinnamon

1 Toast crumpet; top with raspberries and drizzle with honey. Sprinkle with cinnamon to serve.

Test Kitchen NOTES

This recipe is slightly over the breakfast calorie allowance, so choose a recipe for lunch or dinner that has fewer calories or, if you're not feeling too hungry, just have another snack at lunch or dinner instead. You can replace the raspberries with the same weight of sliced strawberries or banana.

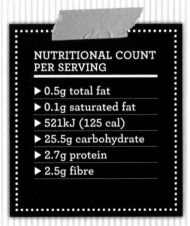

NUTRITIONAL COUNT PER SERVING

▶ 0.5g total fat
▶ 0.1g saturated fat
▶ 521kJ (125 cal)
▶ 25.5g carbohydrate
▶ 2.7g protein
▶ 2.5g fibre

Instead of cinnamon, play around with your favourite spices until you find one you like best to sprinkle on the crumpets. Combination spices, such as allspice or mixed spice, would work well.

baked bean and ricotta-stuffed mushroom

PREP + COOK TIME 10 MINUTES • SERVES 1

**NUTRITIONAL COUNT
PER SERVING**

- ▶ 2g total fat
- ▶ 1g saturated fat
- ▶ 397kJ (94 cal)
- ▶ 8.8g carbohydrate
- ▶ 8.5g protein
- ▶ 4.3g fibre

1 flat mushroom (80g)

1 teaspoon water

60g (2 ounces) canned baked beans in tomato sauce

25g (¾ ounce) low-fat ricotta cheese

2 teaspoons coarsely chopped fresh flat-leaf parsley leaves

1 Preheat grill (broiler) to high. Line a small oven tray with aluminium foil. Place the mushroom, stem-side up, on the tray. Season.
2 Sprinkle the water over the mushroom; grill for 5 minutes or until softened slightly.
3 Top the mushroom with beans and ricotta; grill a further 3 minutes or until golden. Sprinkle with parsley; season to taste.

Leftover baked beans can be frozen in a ziptop plastic bag or an airtight container.

raspberry and almond smoothie

100g (3 ounces) frozen raspberries

1 cup (250ml) unsweetened almond milk

1 teaspoon vanilla extract

1 Blend ingredients until smooth. Pour into a tall glass; serve immediately.

Test Kitchen NOTES

Replace raspberries with the same amount of your favourite frozen berries and a pinch of ground cinnamon or mixed spice for a variation. If you have a nut allergy, substitute almond milk with rice or soy milk – the calorie count will be slightly higher so choose a lighter lunch or dinner.

NUTRITIONAL COUNT PER SERVING

▶ 3.8g total fat
▶ 0.3g saturated fat
▶ 409kJ (97 cal)
▶ 8.8g carbohydrate
▶ 2.7g protein
▶ 6.8g fibre

spicy zucchini omelette

PREP + COOK TIME 10 MINUTES • SERVES 1

cooking-oil spray

1 small zucchini (90g), sliced thinly

2 egg whites

1 tablespoon skim milk

2 teaspoons finely chopped fresh dill

¼ teaspoon chilli flakes

1 teaspoon small fresh dill fronds

1 Lightly spray a small non-stick frying pan with oil; cook zucchini over medium heat for 5 minutes or until golden, turning halfway through cooking time.

2 Meanwhile, whisk egg whites, milk, dill and chilli in a small bowl until frothy; season. Add the egg whites to the pan with zucchini, swirl to coat base of pan; cook for 2 minutes or until just set. Gently fold omelette in half; turn onto a plate. Sprinkle with dill fronds. Serve with a lemon wedge, if you like.

This is also nice as a simple lunch, just serve with a green salad.

NUTRITIONAL COUNT PER SERVING

▶ 1.3g total fat
▶ 0.1g saturated fat
▶ 257kJ (61 cal)
▶ 2.7g carbohydrate
▶ 8.8g protein
▶ 1.6g fibre

cinnamon and pear porridge

PREP + COOK TIME 10 MINUTES • SERVES 1

¼ cup (20g) traditional rolled oats

½ cup (125ml) water

¼ teaspoon ground cinnamon

30g (1 ounce) ripe pear, grated coarsely

6 blueberries

1 Combine oats, water and cinnamon in a small saucepan. Bring to the boil; cook, stirring, for 2 minutes or until porridge has thickened and is tender.

2 Remove porridge from heat, stir through pear; top with blueberries to serve.

Test Kitchen NOTES

You could also make the porridge in a microwave oven. Just follow the packet instructions. We used packham pears in this recipe but you can use your favourite variety when in season. Toss the pear in a small amount of lemon juice to prevent it from discolouring.

NUTRITIONAL COUNT PER SERVING

▶ 1.7g total fat
▶ 0.3g saturated fat
▶ 413kJ (99 cal)
▶ 16.7g carbohydrate
▶ 2.3g protein
▶ 3.3g fibre

Replace the sumac with chinese five-spice and freshly ground black pepper. If you prefer a big breakfast to start your day, add extra toast — 1 slice of toast will add an extra 188kJ (45 cal) to this breakfast.

soft-boiled egg with sumac salt

PREP + COOK TIME 10 MINUTES • SERVES 1

1 egg

½ teaspoon sesame seeds, toasted

¼ teaspoon sumac

pinch sea salt flakes

¼ piece wholemeal bread (12g), toasted, cut into fingers

1 Cook egg in a small saucepan of boiling water for 6 minutes for soft boiled.
2 Combine sesame seeds, sumac and salt in a small bowl. Serve egg with salt and a toast soldier.

NUTRITIONAL COUNT PER SERVING

▶ 5.3g total fat
▶ 1.7g saturated fat
▶ 370kJ (88 cal)
▶ 3.7g carbohydrate
▶ 7.5g protein
▶ 0.4g fibre

spinach and dukkah with tofu

2 x 1cm (½-inch) slices firm tofu (70g)

40g (1½ ounces) baby spinach

1 tablespoon water

½ teaspoon pistachio dukkah

1 Cook tofu in a small non-stick frying pan over medium heat for 1 minute each side or until browned lightly. Remove from pan; cover to keep warm.
2 Add spinach and the water to the pan; cook, stirring, for 2 minutes or until spinach is wilted.
3 Top tofu with spinach; sprinkle with dukkah.

Test Kitchen NOTES

Sprinkle with za'atar or chilli flakes for an alternative flavour. This is slightly more than the breakfast allowance, so choose another meal with slightly lower calories for lunch or dinner or, if you're not feeling too hungry, just have a snack.

NUTRITIONAL COUNT PER SERVING

▶ 6.2g total fat
▶ 0.8g saturated fat
▶ 452kJ (108 cal)
▶ 0.5g carbohydrate
▶ 9.8g protein
▶ 5.6g fibre

beetroot, ginger and apple juice

PREP TIME 10 MINUTES • SERVES 1

2 baby beetroot (beets) (50g), chopped roughly

1 small apple (130g), cored, quartered

1 lime (90g), peeled

¼ cup loosely packed fresh mint leaves

1 Push ingredients through a juice extractor into a glass. Stir to combine.

Replace the apple with carrot and the lime with orange. Serve over ice, if you like.

NUTRITIONAL COUNT PER SERVING

▶ 0.3g total fat
▶ 0.2g saturated fat
▶ 323kJ (77 cal)
▶ 14.2g carbohydrate
▶ 2.3g protein
▶ 0.4g fibre

baked beans on rye toast

PREP + COOK TIME 5 MINUTES • SERVES 1

½ x 130g (4-ounce) can baked beans in tomato sauce

½ slice dark rye bread (23g), toasted

pinch chilli flakes

1 Heat baked beans in a small saucepan over low heat for 2 minutes until heated through; stirring occasionally.

2 Spoon baked beans over toast; sprinkle with chilli flakes.

For a different flavour, sprinkle with chopped chives and strips of lemon rind.

NUTRITIONAL COUNT PER SERVING

▶ 0.8g total fat
▶ 0.1g saturated fat
▶ 411kJ (98 cal)
▶ 16.2g carbohydrate
▶ 4.7g protein
▶ 4.6g fibre

lunch

tuna, carrot and zucchini salad with pitta chips

PREP + COOK TIME 10 MINUTES • SERVES 1

¼ wholemeal pitta bread (20g), torn

95g (3 ounces) canned tuna in springwater, drained

50g (1½ ounces) carrot, sliced thinly

1 small zucchini (90g), sliced thinly

1½ tablespoons finely chopped fresh chives

2 teaspoons lime juice

2 tablespoons light tzatziki dip

1 Preheat oven to 200°C/400°F.

2 Place pitta on an oven rack. Cook for 5 minutes or until crisp; cool.

3 Combine tuna, carrot, zucchini, chives and juice in a medium bowl; season to taste. Serve with the pitta chips and tzatziki.

NUTRITIONAL COUNT PER SERVING

▶ 3.2g total fat
▶ 0.6g saturated fat
▶ 844kJ (202 cal)
▶ 19.6g carbohydrate
▶ 21.1g protein
▶ 4.6g fibre

Test Kitchen NOTES

Make lots of pitta chips and store in an airtight container to have with dips, soups etc. You can grill (broil) the pitta bread; just make sure you keep a close eye on it so it doesn't burn. If making the salad ahead of time, just leave off the lime juice and tzatziki until ready to serve. Use a julienne peeler to thinly slice the carrot and zucchini.

Test Kitchen
NOTES
Toast the walnuts to add extra flavour and crunch to the salad. In place of the nuts and ricotta, you could substitute 95g (3 ounces) canned drained tuna in springwater. If you like, combine the salad with the spicy zucchini omelette (page 20) for an easy dinner.

radish and lentil salad

15g (½ ounce) mesclun

3 red radishes (60g), trimmed, sliced thinly

1 green onion (scallion), sliced thinly

50g (1½ ounces) cherry tomatoes, halved

30g (1 ounce) snow peas, sliced thinly on
the diagonal

½ cup (115g) rinsed, drained canned brown lentils

1 tablespoon lemon juice

½ long red chilli, sliced thinly

1 tablespoon low-fat ricotta

10g (½ ounces) walnuts, chopped coarsely

1 Combine mesclun, radish, onion, tomato,
snow peas and lentils in a large bowl.
2 Combine juice and chilli, drizzle over salad;
toss gently to combine.
3 Sprinkle salad with ricotta and walnuts; season
to taste.

**NUTRITIONAL COUNT
PER SERVING**

► 8.9g total fat
► 1.3g saturated fat
► 923kJ (220 cal)
► 17g carbohydrate
► 14g protein
► 7.9g fibre

*Mesclun is a mixture of assorted young
lettuce and other green leaves; it is also
sold as salad mix or gourmet salad mix.*

vegie hash with kale, chickpeas and poached egg

PREP + COOK TIME 25 MINUTES • SERVES 1

¼ small kumara (orange-sweet potato) (62g), chopped into 2cm (¾-inch) pieces

50g (1½ ounces) broccolini, trimmed

2 teaspoons white vinegar

1 egg (59g)

cooking-oil spray

1 fresh small red thai (serrano) chilli, chopped finely

½ clove garlic, crushed

25g (¾ ounce) canned chickpeas (garbanzo), rinsed, drained

25g (¾ ounce) kale, torn

2 tablespoons water

2 teaspoons white chia seeds

1 Boil, steam or microwave kumara and broccolini, separately, until tender.

2 Meanwhile, half-fill a small saucepan with water, add vinegar; bring to the boil. Using a wooden spoon, make a whirlpool in the water; slide the egg into the whirlpool. Cover pan, turn off heat; stand for 3 minutes or until a light film of egg white sets over egg yolk (or until cooked how you like it). Using a slotted spoon, remove egg from the pan; drain on absorbent paper. Cover to keep warm.

3 Spray a large frying pan lightly with oil over high heat. Add chilli, garlic, chickpeas, kumara and broccolini; cook, stirring, for 1 minute or until heated through.

4 Add kale and the water to the pan; cook, stirring for 1 minute or until kale is wilted. Season to taste.

5 Sprinkle the vegetables with chia seeds and top with egg; serve immediately.

NUTRITIONAL COUNT PER SERVING

▶ 7.4g total fat
▶ 1.9g saturated fat
▶ 857kJ (205 cal)
▶ 17.5g carbohydrate
▶ 13.1g protein
▶ 7.2g fibre

You can use spinach or silver beet instead of kale.

Test Kitchen
NOTES

Leftover chickpeas can
be stored in a small bowl,
covered and refrigerated,
for up to 2 days. Use leftover
chickpeas in salads, stirred
through roast vegetables or
curries. Remove the seeds
from the chilli if you prefer
a milder heat; the seeds and
membranes contain the heat
of the chilli. To check the heat
of a chilli, try tasting a chilli
seed on its own before cooking.

The miso soup can be made and placed in an insulated flask for a portable lunch. Continue from step 2 at lunch.

chicken miso soup

chicken miso soup

1 x 18g (½ ounce) packet instant miso soup with wakame

30g (1 ounce) rice vermicelli

100g (1½ ounces) shredded cooked chicken

1 cup (250ml) boiling water

40g (1½ ounce) baby spinach leaves, chopped

1 green onion (scallion), sliced thinly diagonally

1 teaspoon thinly sliced fresh long red chilli

1 Combine miso, vermicelli, chicken and the boiling water in a medium saucepan; cook over low heat, stirring, for 5 minutes or until vermicelli are tender.

2 Stir through spinach, onion and chilli.

NUTRITIONAL COUNT PER SERVING

▶ 9.7g total fat
▶ 4.8g saturated fat
▶ 1017kJ (243 cal)
▶ 25g carbohydrate
▶ 12.5g protein
▶ 2.8g fibre

margarita pressed pizza

1 tablespoon tomato paste

1 x 20cm (8-inch) floured tortilla (40g)

50g (1½ ounces) cherry tomatoes, sliced thinly

6 fresh basil leaves

6 baby bocconcini (30g), sliced thinly

1 Preheat a sandwich press.

2 Spread tomato paste over half of the tortilla, leaving a 1cm (½-inch) border. Top with tomato, basil and bocconcini. Season.

3 Fold over to enclose filling. Lightly wrap tortilla in baking paper; place in sandwich press. Cook for 3 minutes or until golden and cheese has melted. Cut into wedges to serve.

Photograph page 34

NUTRITIONAL COUNT PER SERVING

▶ 4.2g total fat
▶ 1.3g saturated fat
▶ 810kJ (194 cal)
▶ 6.9g carbohydrate
▶ 30.9g protein
▶ 1.4g fibre

margarita pressed pizza
recipe page 33

*Serve topped with extra basil
leaves or baby rocket leaves.*

hot-smoked salmon and
egg salad, recipe page 36

hot-smoked salmon and egg salad

PREP + COOK TIME 35 MINUTES • SERVES 1

80g (2½ ounces) pumpkin, chopped coarsely

olive-oil cooking spray

1 egg (59g)

30g (1 ounce) mesclun

¼ small red onion (25g), sliced thinly

1 baby beetroot (beet) (25g), peeled, sliced thinly

1 tablespoon lemon juice

50g (1½ ounces) hot smoked salmon, flaked

2 teaspoons pepitas

1 Preheat oven to 220°C/425°F.
2 Place pumpkin on a baking-paper-lined tray; spray pumpkin with oil. Bake for 25 minutes or until golden and tender. Cool slightly.
3 Meanwhile, place egg in a small saucepan of cold water; bring to the boil, boil for 2 minutes. Remove egg from the water with a slotted spoon; when cool enough to handle, shell egg. Cut egg in half.
4 Combine mesclun, onion, beetroot and juice in a small bowl. Serve salad topped with pumpkin, salmon and egg; sprinkle with pepitas, season to taste.

Photograph page 35

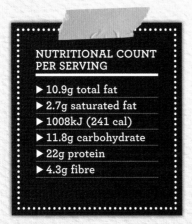

NUTRITIONAL COUNT PER SERVING
▶ 10.9g total fat
▶ 2.7g saturated fat
▶ 1008kJ (241 cal)
▶ 11.8g carbohydrate
▶ 22g protein
▶ 4.3g fibre

poached chicken salad with dijon dressing

PREP + COOK TIME 20 MINUTES • SERVES 1

2 cups (500ml) water

2 teaspoons chicken stock powder

100g (3 ounces) chicken breast fillet

30g (1 ounce) baby rocket leaves (arugula)

50g (1½ ounces) asparagus, trimmed, sliced thinly lengthways

1 green onion (scallion), sliced thinly diagonally

1 tablespoon white wine vinegar

½ teaspoon dijon mustard

½ teaspoon honey

1 teaspoon natural flaked almonds

1 Combine the water and stock powder in a small saucepan, bring to the boil; add chicken. Simmer, uncovered, over low heat, for 10 minutes or until chicken is cooked. Cool chicken in poaching liquid for 10 minutes; drain, then slice thinly.
2 Combine chicken in a medium bowl with rocket, asparagus and onion; season to taste.
3 Place vinegar, mustard and honey in a screw-top jar; shake well; drizzle over salad. To serve, sprinkle with nuts, and strips of lemon rind, if you like.

Test Kitchen NOTES

This recipe makes a great portable lunch; separate the salad, dressing and nuts, and assemble at lunch time. You can use a V-slicer or mandoline to thinly slice the asparagus.

poached chicken salad
with dijon dressing

curried vegetable soup

2 cups (500ml) reduced-salt vegetable stock

1 small brown onion (80g), chopped coarsely

1 teaspoon finely grated fresh ginger

1 clove garlic, crushed

2 teaspoons rogan josh curry paste

1 small carrot (130g), chopped coarsely

¾ cup (180ml) water

85g (3 ounces) canned chickpeas (garbanzo), rinsed, drained

60g (2 ounces) green beans, trimmed

2 tablespoons fresh coriander leaves (cilantro)

6 mini pappadums (5g)

2 tablespoons low-fat natural yoghurt

1 Combine ½ cup stock, onion, ginger and garlic in a medium saucepan; bring to the boil. Reduce heat to medium; cook, stirring occasionally, for 5 minutes or until onion softens.

2 Add curry paste; cook, stirring, for 30 seconds or until fragrant. Reduce heat to low, add carrot; cook, stirring, for 5 minutes. Add remaining stock and the water; bring to the boil. Reduce heat; simmer, covered, for 10 minutes.

3 Add chickpeas and beans to pan; simmer, covered, for 5 minutes or until beans are tender. Stir in half the coriander. Stand soup for 10 minutes.

4 Meanwhile, microwave pappadums according to packet directions.

5 Blend or process soup until smooth. Serve topped with remaining coriander leaves; accompany with yoghurt and pappadums.

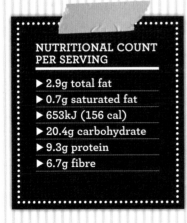

NUTRITIONAL COUNT PER SERVING

▶ 2.9g total fat
▶ 0.7g saturated fat
▶ 653kJ (156 cal)
▶ 20.4g carbohydrate
▶ 9.3g protein
▶ 6.7g fibre

Reheat the soup, covered, in a microwave oven on HIGH (100%) for about 1½ minutes, stirring halfway through the heating time.

salmon pitta pizza

**NUTRITIONAL COUNT
PER SERVING**

▶ 5.1g total fat
▶ 1.6g saturated fat
▶ 1027kJ (245 cal)
▶ 36.4g carbohydrate
▶ 10.2g protein
▶ 6.1g fibre

1 wholemeal pitta pocket bread (70g)

olive-oil cooking spray

50g (1½ ounces) smoked salmon

25g (¾ ounce) low-fat ricotta

½ baby fennel bulb (65g), sliced thinly

20g (1½ ounces) baby rocket leaves (arugula)

1 teaspoon finely shredded lemon rind

1 lemon wedge

1 Preheat grill (broiler) on medium heat.
2 Place pitta on an oven tray; lightly spray with oil. Place under grill for 1 minute or until browned lightly and crisp.
3 Arrange salmon, ricotta, fennel and rocket on pitta; season to taste. To serve, sprinkle with rind and accompany with wedge.

You can replace the rocket with baby spinach leaves. Use a mandoline or V-slicer to slice the fennel.

roasted mushroom bruschetta

PREP + COOK TIME 20 MINUTES • SERVES 1

2 large portobello mushrooms (150g)

1 teaspoon olive oil

1 teaspoon white wine vinegar

1 clove garlic, crushed

2 teaspoons chopped fresh tarragon

1 slice sourdough bread (45g)

25g (¾ ounce) low-fat ricotta

15g (¾ ounce) rocket leaves (arugula), coarsely torn

1 Preheat oven to 180°C/375°F.

2 Place mushrooms on an oiled oven tray. Drizzle with oil and vinegar; sprinkle with garlic and tarragon, season.

3 Roast in oven for 10 minutes, then cover with foil and roast for a further 5 minutes or until tender. Remove mushrooms from oven; set aside to cool slightly, then halve.

4 Meanwhile, lightly spray bread with oil; place on a heated grill pan (or grill or barbecue). Grill for 2 minutes each side or until browned lightly and grill marks show.

5 Spread toast with ricotta, top with rocket and mushrooms; sprinkle with extra tarragon, if you like.

You can replace the tarragon with thyme leaves and the rocket with baby spinach.

NUTRITIONAL COUNT PER SERVING

▶ 7.7g total fat
▶ 1.9g saturated fat
▶ 992kJ (237 cal)
▶ 25.7g carbohydrate
▶ 13.8g protein
▶ 4.5g fibre

lamb kofta plate

60g (2 ounces) minced (ground) lamb

½ teaspoon each ground cumin and coriander

½ clove garlic, crushed

75g (2½ ounces) red cabbage, sliced thinly

½ cup firmly packed fresh flat-leaf parsley leaves, chopped roughly

2 teaspoons lemon juice

1 tablespoon baba ghanoush dip

1 medium gherkin (30g), sliced thinly lengthways

1 lemon wedge

1 Combine mince, spices and garlic in a small bowl; season.

2 Heat a small non-stick frying pan over medium heat. Shape mince mixture into two patties; cook for 3 minutes each side or until cooked through.

3 Meanwhile, combine cabbage, parsley and juice in a small bowl; season to taste.

4 Serve patties with cabbage salad, baba ghanoush, gherkin and lemon.

NUTRITIONAL COUNT PER SERVING

▶ 11.7g total fat

▶ 3.7g saturated fat

▶ 994kJ (238 cal)

▶ 11.8g carbohydrate

▶ 17.5g protein

▶ 6.7g fibre

Test Kitchen NOTES

There is no need to make two different lunches when serving this delicious kofta plate – everyone will want a taste, not believing it's a diet lunch. Just double or triple the recipe so everyone gets their own!

Shape the patties ahead of time; cover and store in the fridge. Any spare lamb mince can be frozen. You could also use light hummus instead of baba ghanoush.

crushed potato and pea salad with poached egg

200g (6½ ounces) baby new (chat) potatoes

¼ cup (30g) frozen peas

½ green onion (scallion), sliced thinly diagonally

1 egg (59g)

20g (¾ ounce) snow pea sprouts, trimmed

MUSTARD DRESSING

2 tablespoons apple cider vinegar

1 teaspoon dijon mustard

1 teaspoon wholegrain mustard

2 teaspoons finely chopped fresh flat-leaf parsley

1 Boil, steam or microwave potato and peas, separately until tender; drain. Combine potatoes and peas in a medium bowl; crush lightly using a potato masher. Toss through white part of onion.

2 Half fill a small shallow frying pan with water; bring to the boil. Break egg into a cup, slide into the pan; return water to the boil.

3 Cover pan, turn off heat; stand for 3 minutes or until a light film of egg white sets over egg yolk. Remove egg using a slotted spoon; place spoon on an absorbent-paper-lined plate briefly to blot up poaching liquid.

4 Meanwhile, make mustard dressing. Add dressing to hot potato mixture, toss gently to combine.

5 Serve salad topped with sprouts and poached egg; season to taste.

MUSTARD DRESSING Combine ingredients in a screw-top jar; shake well.

NUTRITIONAL COUNT PER SERVING

▶ 5.3g total fat
▶ 1.7g saturated fat
▶ 995kJ (237 cal)
▶ 27.7g carbohydrate
▶ 14.1g protein
▶ 6.7g fibre

lemon and dill chickpea salad

1½ tablespoons mixed colour quinoa

1 cup (250ml) water

80g (2½ ounces) canned chickpeas (garbanzo), rinsed, drained

100g (3 ounces) lebanese cucumber, seeded, sliced thinly crossways

100g (3 ounces) mixed heirloom cherry tomatoes, halved (or quartered if large)

15g (½ ounce) light greek fetta cheese, crumbled

1 tablespoon coarsely chopped fresh dill

1 teaspoon finely grated lemon rind

2 teaspoons lemon juice

½ clove garlic, crushed

1 Rinse quinoa well, drain. Place quinoa and the water in a small saucepan; bring to the boil. Reduce heat to medium; cook, uncovered, for 12 minutes or until tender. Drain; rinse under cold water until cool, drain well.

2 Combine chickpeas, quinoa, cucumber, tomato, fetta, dill, juice, rind and garlic in a medium bowl; toss gently, season to taste.

NUTRITIONAL COUNT PER SERVING

▶ 5.6g total fat
▶ 2g saturated fat
▶ 1035kJ (247 cal)
▶ 30.5g carbohydrate
▶ 13.4g protein
▶ 8.2g fibre

You can use cherry tomatoes for this recipe if you can't find mixed heirloom cherry tomatoes.

Test Kitchen
NOTES
You can make this salad ahead of time; keep the lemon juice separate until ready to serve. If you're having trouble finding mixed coloured quinoa, buy white and black quinoa and mix it yourself. Remove the seeds of the cucumber with a teaspoon.

crab and corn soup

NUTRITIONAL COUNT PER SERVING

- ▶ 2.5g total fat
- ▶ 0.5g saturated fat
- ▶ 892kJ (213 cal)
- ▶ 23.3g carbohydrate
- ▶ 22.3g protein
- ▶ 4.5g fibre

1 cup (250ml) chicken or vegetable stock

100g (3 ounces) fresh crab meat

125g (4 ounces) canned creamed corn

½ teaspoon finely grated fresh ginger

½ teaspoon soy sauce

2 green onions (scallion), sliced thinly

1 egg white

1 tablespoon water

1 Heat stock in a small saucepan over high heat; bring to a simmer. Reduce heat to low; add crab, corn, ginger, sauce and half the onion, stir to combine. Season.

2 Whisk egg white with the water in a small jug. While continually stirring the crab mixture, pour the egg white into the pan in a thin, steady stream. Cook for 1 minute or until egg white is set.

3 Serve soup topped with remaining onion.

Replace the crab meat with 100g of finely shredded cooked chicken breast.

quinoa and pea tabbouleh

PREP + COOK TIME 20 MINUTES • SERVES 1

¼ cup (50g) quinoa

2 cups (500ml) water

¼ cup (30g) frozen peas, thawed

1 small tomato, chopped finely

¼ cup fresh flat-leaf parsley leaves

2 tablespoons torn fresh mint leaves

1 tablespoon lemon juice

1 Rinse quinoa well, drain. Combine quinoa and the water in a small saucepan; bring to the boil. Reduce heat to low; cook, covered, for 10 minutes or until quinoa is tender. Refresh under cold running water. Drain, pressing quinoa with the back of a spoon to remove as much liquid as possible.

2 Meanwhile, cook peas in a small saucepan of boiling water for 2 minutes or until tender. Refresh under cold running water. Drain well.

3 Combine quinoa, peas, tomato, parsley, mint and juice in a small bowl. Season to taste.

Use red or black quinoa for a different look. Fresh peas can be used when in season.

NUTRITIONAL COUNT PER SERVING
- ▶ 3.4g total fat
- ▶ 0.4g saturated fat
- ▶ 1063kJ (254 cal)
- ▶ 38.7g carbohydrate
- ▶ 11.7g protein
- ▶ 10.1g fibre

Quesadilla can also be cooked in an electric sandwich press; wrap lightly in baking paper and toast for 3 minutes or until toasted and heated through.

pumpkin and corn quesadilla with fresh tomato salsa

PREP + COOK TIME 15 MINUTES • SERVES 1

100g (3 ounces) pumpkin, chopped coarsely

1 tablespoon water

¼ cup (40g) corn kernels

¼ teaspoon chilli flakes

½ clove garlic, crushed

25g (¾ ounce) grated extra-light cheddar

1 x 28g (17cm) corn tortilla

1 small vine-ripened tomato (90g), chopped finely

¼ small red onion (25g), chopped finely

¼ cup firmly packed fresh coriander leaves (cilantro)

2 teaspoons lime juice

1 Place pumpkin and the water in a medium microwave-safe dish. Microwave on HIGH (100%) for 5 minutes or until tender. Mash pumpkin; season to taste.

2 Add corn, chilli, garlic and grated cheese to pumpkin; season.

3 Heat a small non-stick frying pan over medium heat. Place tortilla into pan; warm gently for 1 minute or until pliable.

4 Spread pumpkin mixture over one half of the warmed tortilla while still in pan. Fold over to enclose (tortilla may break at this stage if not warmed through). Cook quesadilla for 2 minutes each side or until golden and cooked through.

5 Meanwhile, combine tomato, onion, coriander and juice in a small bowl; season to taste. Serve quesadilla with the tomato salsa.

NUTRITIONAL COUNT PER SERVING

▶ 5.8g total fat
▶ 2.7g saturated fat
▶ 1023kJ (244 cal)
▶ 27.9g carbohydrate
▶ 14.8g protein
▶ 9.1g fibre

roasted tomato and cumin soup

PREP + COOK TIME 1 HOUR • SERVES 4

Test Kitchen NOTES

This soup makes enough for 4 serves. Freeze the remaining soup in 1½-cup portions in ziptop plastic bags or airtight containers.

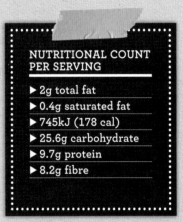

NUTRITIONAL COUNT PER SERVING

▸ 2g total fat
▸ 0.4g saturated fat
▸ 745kJ (178 cal)
▸ 25.6g carbohydrate
▸ 9.7g protein
▸ 8.2g fibre

1kg (2 pounds) vine-ripened tomatoes, halved
2 large red onions (600g), skin on, quartered
6 cloves garlic, unpeeled
⅓ cup loosely packed fresh oregano leaves
2 teaspoons cumin seeds
3 cups (750ml) vegetable stock
¼ wholemeal pitta bread (20g)
1 tablespoon fat-free natural yoghurt

1 Preheat oven to 200°C/400°F.
2 Line a roasting pan with baking paper. Place tomato, onion, garlic, oregano and cumin in the pan; season. Roast, uncovered, for 45 minutes or until the vegetables are tender and browned.
3 Peel onion and garlic; combine in a large saucepan with tomato, oregano, cumin and stock. Blend with a stick blender until smooth. Bring to the boil; boil until heated through.
4 Meanwhile, place pitta on an oven rack in oven; cook for 5 minutes or until crisp. Cool, then break pitta into irregular pieces.
5 Pour 1½ cups soup into a bowl; dollop with yoghurt, serve with pitta toasts (see tip, opposite page).

While the soup serves 4, the pitta bread and yoghurt is for one serving only. When reheating the soup, bake more pitta toasts and serve with extra yoghurt.

spiced cauliflower

◄ PREP + COOK TIME 35 MINUTES • SERVES 1 ►

¼ small cauliflower (250g), cut into florets

olive-oil cooking spray

¼ teaspoon each ground cinnamon, cumin, coriander and turmeric

2 tablespoons sunflower seeds

1 tablespoon currants

¼ cup fresh coriander leaves (cilantro)

¼ cup fresh mint leaves

3 teaspoons lemon juice

1 tablespoon reduced-fat greek-style yoghurt

1 Preheat oven to 180°C/375°F. Line an oven tray with baking paper.

2 Place cauliflower on tray; lightly spray with oil. Sprinkle with combined spices; season. Toss to coat. Roast for 15 minutes or until cauliflower is tender. Sprinkle with sunflower seeds; roast for a further 10 minutes or until toasted.

3 Combine cauliflower mixture with currants, coriander, mint and juice in a medium bowl; toss to combine, season to taste. Serve with yoghurt.

You can replace the spices with a Moroccan spice mixture.

NUTRITIONAL COUNT PER SERVING

▶ 10.4g total fat
▶ 1.8g saturated fat
▶ 1002kJ (239 cal)
▶ 21.4g carbohydrate
▶ 10.5g protein
▶ 9.5g fibre

tuna, celery and radish rice salad

PREP + COOK TIME 5 MINUTES • SERVES 1

½ cup (80g) microwave brown rice

95g (3 ounces) canned tuna in springwater, drained, flaked

1 trimmed celery stalk (100g), sliced thinly

1 trimmed red radish (15g), sliced thinly

1 tablespoon lemon juice

2 teaspoons finely chopped fresh dill

1 Cook rice according to directions on packet (save the remaining rice for another day).
2 Combine rice, tuna, celery, radish, juice and dill in a small bowl; toss to combine.

For a different flavour, replace the dill with fresh basil, and add thin strips of lemon rind with the juice.

banana and strawberry smoothie

200g (6½ ounces) fat-free natural yoghurt

1 small banana (130g), chopped coarsely

100g (3 ounces) strawberries, chopped

½ cup crushed ice

1 Blend yoghurt, banana, strawberries and ice until smooth. Pour into a serving glass.

You can replace the strawberries with raspberries or blackberries.

NUTRITIONAL COUNT PER SERVING

▶ 0.5g total fat
▶ 0g saturated fat
▶ 880kJ (210 cal)
▶ 27.7g carbohydrate
▶ 21.3g protein
▶ 3.4g fibre

pesto turkey couscous salad

20g (¾ ounce) israeli couscous

100g (3 ounces) asparagus, sliced thinly diagonally

80g (2½ ounces) sliced cooked turkey breast, chopped coarsely

20g (¾ ounce) red onion, sliced thinly

1 tablespoon small fresh basil leaves

HEALTHY BASIL PESTO

2 cups firmly packed fresh basil leaves

1 tablespoon blanched almonds

2 tablespoons finely grated parmesan

1 clove garlic, crushed

⅓ cup (80ml) water

1 tablespoon lemon juice

1 Cook couscous in a small saucepan of boiling water for 7 minutes or until just tender. Add asparagus; cook for 1 minute. Drain; rinse under cold water until cool.

2 Meanwhile, make healthy basil pesto.

3 Combine couscous, asparagus, turkey, onion and basil with 1½ tablespoons of the pesto; season to taste.

HEALTHY BASIL PESTO Blend or process ingredients until smooth; season to taste.

Use pearl couscous if you can't find israeli couscous in the international food section of the supermarket.

NUTRITIONAL COUNT PER SERVING

▶ 5.8g total fat
▶ 1.6g saturated fat
▶ 873kJ (209 cal)
▶ 8.8g carbohydrate
▶ 28.4g protein
▶ 3g fibre

Test Kitchen
NOTES

The pesto makes enough for 4 serves. Divide the pesto into 1½-tablespoon portions and freeze in small ziptop plastic bags or airtight containers. You can use the remaining pesto on a non-fasting day tossed through pasta or as a base for your favourite pizza. Make the salad ahead of time, but add the pesto just before serving. You can find sliced turkey breast in the deli section at supermarkets. You could also use shredded cooked chicken, if you prefer.

roast beef and beetroot relish open sandwich

PREP + COOK TIME 15 MINUTES • SERVES 1

NUTRITIONAL COUNT PER SERVING

▶ 5.2g total fat
▶ 1.3g saturated fat
▶ 1027kJ (245 cal)
▶ 24.5g carbohydrate
▶ 21.1g protein
▶ 6.7g fibre

½ small beetroot (beet) (50g), grated coarsely

½ small red onion (50g), chopped finely

1 tablespoon red wine vinegar

1 slice wholemeal bread (45g)

2 teaspoons light hummus

70g (2½ ounces) rare roast beef, sliced thinly

10g (½ ounce) rocket (arugula)

1 teaspoon finely chopped fresh chives

1 teaspoon lemon juice

1 Combine beetroot, onion and vinegar in a small saucepan; bring to the boil. Reduce heat; simmer, stirring occasionally, for 10 minutes or until liquid has reduced and beetroot is tender. Season to taste.
2 Spread bread with hummus, top with beef, rocket, beetroot, chives and drizzle with juice; season to taste.

Swap mountain bread for the wholemeal bread and serve as a wrap for those times when you need lunch on the go.

ham, asparagus and lemon ricotta wrap

50g (1½ ounces) asparagus, trimmed, sliced in half lengthways

2 tablespoons reduced-fat ricotta

½ teaspoon finely grated lemon rind

2 mountain breads (50g)

50g (2½ ounces) thinly sliced lite ham

15g (½ ounce) trimmed watercress

1 teaspoon lemon juice

1 Boil, steam or microwave asparagus until tender, drain; refresh under cold water. Pat dry with absorbent paper.

2 Combine ricotta and rind in a small bowl; season to taste.

3 Place breads on top of each other on a board. Spread top piece of bread with ricotta mixture; top with asparagus, ham and watercress. Sprinkle with juice; season to taste. Roll up breads to serve.

Test Kitchen NOTES

Asparagus and ricotta can be prepared a day ahead; store, covered, in the fridge. You need 1 lemon for this recipe. We used two pieces of mountain bread to wrap the filling as one piece tends to split. Add the lemon juice just before serving.

NUTRITIONAL COUNT PER SERVING

▶ 5.3g total fat
▶ 2.4g saturated fat
▶ 1045kJ (250 cal)
▶ 28.7g carbohydrate
▶ 20.1g protein
▶ 2.7g fibre

asian chilli lamb salad

PREP + COOK TIME 15 MINUTES (+REFRIGERATION) • SERVES 1

100g (3 ounces) lamb backstrap, trimmed

1 clove garlic, crushed

2 tablespoons lime juice

2½ tablespoons fish sauce

2 fresh small red thai (serrano) chillies, chopped finely

½ small red onion (40g), sliced thinly

2 tablespoons fresh coriander leaves (cilantro)

2 tablespoons fresh small mint leaves

½ small lebanese cucumber (65g), cut into ribbons

30g (1 ounce) asian salad leaf mix

1 Combine lamb, garlic and half each of the juice, sauce and chilli in a medium bowl. Cover; refrigerate for 30 minutes.

2 Combine 2 teaspoons of the remaining juice and the onion in a small bowl, set aside.

3 Drain lamb from marinade, season. Cook lamb on a lightly oiled grill plate (or grill or barbecue) over medium heat for 3 minutes each side or until cooked as desired.

4 Place lamb in a medium bowl, add remaining sauce, juice and chilli to bowl; cover, stand for 10 minutes. Slice lamb thinly, return to bowl.

5 Add onion mixture to lamb with herbs, cucumber and salad mix. Season to taste.

NUTRITIONAL COUNT PER SERVING

▶ 8.5g total fat
▶ 2.4g saturated fat
▶ 975kJ (233 cal)
▶ 7.6g carbohydrate
▶ 28.3g protein
▶ 4.5g fibre

For a portable lunch, keep the lamb and its juice separate from the salad; toss together before serving.

dinner

chilli prawns with green apple salsa

PREP + COOK TIME 15 MINUTES • SERVES 1

1 long green chilli

6 medium green prawns (shrimp) (250g), shelled

1 garlic clove, crushed

2 tablespoons lime juice

1 white corn tortilla (46g)

½ small green apple (65g), cored, cut into matchsticks

1 green onion (scallion), sliced thinly

1 tablespoon fresh mint leaves

1 Finely chop half the chilli, thinly slice remaining chilli. Combine prawns, garlic, half the juice and the finely chopped chilli in a small bowl. Cook prawns on a heated oiled grill plate (or grill or barbecue) until just changed in colour. Transfer to a plate; cover to keep warm.

2 Cook tortilla on grill plate for 1 minute each side or until warmed through.

3 Meanwhile, combine apple, onion, thinly sliced chilli, remaining juice and the mint in a small bowl, toss gently.

4 Serve prawns and apple salsa on tortilla.

NUTRITIONAL COUNT PER SERVING

▸ 2.3g total fat
▸ 0.5g saturated fat
▸ 1103kJ (264 cal)
▸ 26.5g carbohydrate
▸ 29.4g protein
▸ 6.4g fibre

Test Kitchen
NOTES

The meatloaf can be made two days ahead; store, covered in the fridge. Reheat in a microwave oven on MEDIUM (50%) until heated through, or wrap the meatloaf in foil and reheat in a moderately-hot oven for 20 minutes or until heated through.

beef and mushroom meatloaf

1 tablespoon vegetable stock

50g (1½ ounces) button mushrooms, chopped finely

2 cloves garlic, crushed

100g (3 ounces) lean minced (ground) beef

1 teaspoon tomato paste

1 teaspoon worcestershire sauce

cooking-oil spray

100g (3 ounces) pumpkin, cut into thin wedges

50g (1½ ounces) spinach

1 Preheat oven to 220°C/425°F. Lightly grease 1 hole of a 6-hole (¾-cup/180ml) texas muffin pan, dariole mould or a ¾ cup (180ml) ovenproof dish.

2 Place stock, mushrooms and half the garlic in a small frying pan over medium heat; cook, stirring occasionally, for 4 minutes or until golden and tender; cool.

3 Combine beef, paste, sauce and mushroom mixture in a small bowl; season. Press mixture into pan hole. Bake for 20 minutes. Turn meatloaf out onto a baking tray; bake for a further 5 minutes or until meatloaf is browned and firm.

4 Meanwhile, lightly spray a medium frying pan with oil; cook pumpkin, covered, over medium heat, for 5 minutes each side or until tender. Remove from pan; cover to keep warm.

5 Serve meatloaf with pumpkin and spinach; season to taste.

NUTRITIONAL COUNT PER SERVING

▸ 11.7g total fat
▸ 4.9g saturated fat
▸ 1210kJ (280 cal)
▸ 11.6g carbohydrate
▸ 31.9g protein
▸ 5.4g fibre

The pumpkin can be swapped with kumara (orange sweet potato).

sour vietnamese soup

PREP + COOK TIME 15 MINUTES • SERVES 1

2 cups (500ml) beef stock

2cm (¾ inch) piece fresh ginger, peeled, sliced into matchsticks

½ fresh long red chilli, sliced thinly

1 tablespoon lime juice

1 teaspoon fish sauce

70g (2½ ounces) beef fillet, sliced thinly

50g (1½ ounces) baby pak choy, leaves separated

30g (1 ounce) rice vermicelli noodles

½ green onion (scallion), sliced thinly

1 tablespoon mint leaves

1 tablespoon coriander leaves (cilantro)

1 Combine stock, ginger and chilli in a medium saucepan; bring to the boil. Reduce heat; simmer, uncovered, for 5 minutes.

2 Add juice, sauce and beef to pan; return to the boil. Add pak choy; cook for 1 minute or until pak choy is wilted. Remove from heat.

3 Meanwhile, place noodles in a small heatproof bowl, cover with boiling water; stand until tender, drain.

4 Place noodles in a medium serving bowl; ladle over soup, top with onion and herbs.

NUTRITIONAL COUNT PER SERVING

▶ 13.3g total fat
▶ 4.9g saturated fat
▶ 1222kJ (292 cal)
▶ 11.2g carbohydrate
▶ 30.5g protein
▶ 3.1g fibre

Test Kitchen NOTES

Replace the baby pak choy with your favourite Asian green. For a little extra heat, slice a small red thai (serrano) chilli and add it to the soup with the herbs. If you prefer chicken, replace the beef stock with chicken stock and the beef with sliced chicken breast.

tomato and zucchini tart

PREP + COOK TIME 1 HOUR • SERVES 1

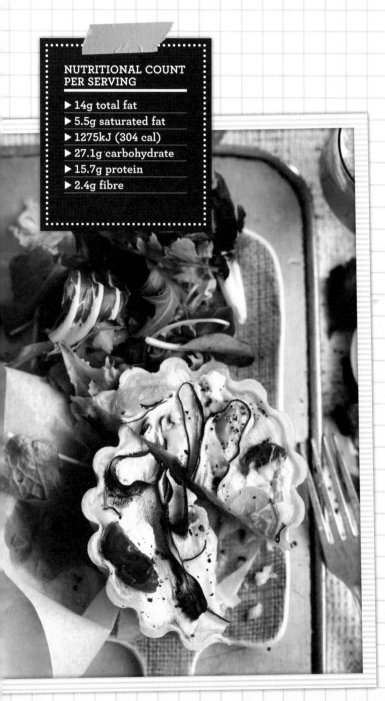

NUTRITIONAL COUNT PER SERVING

▶ 14g total fat
▶ 5.5g saturated fat
▶ 1275kJ (304 cal)
▶ 27.1g carbohydrate
▶ 15.7g protein
▶ 2.4g fibre

cooking-oil spray

¼ sheet reduced-fat shortcrust pastry (50g)

1 egg

1 egg white

2 tablespoons water

50g (1½ ounces) mixed cherry tomatoes, halved

½ small zucchini (45g), cut into thin strips

2 teaspoons low-fat cottage cheese

15g (¾ ounce) mesclun

1 tablespoon fresh flat-leaf parsley leaves

1 tablespoon lemon juice

1 clove garlic, crushed

1 Preheat oven to 200°C/400°F.
2 Spray a round 10.5cm (4-inch) (base measurement) loose-based flan pan lightly with oil. Line pan with pastry, press into sides; trim edges. Place on an oven tray; refrigerate for 10 minutes.
3 Whisk egg, egg white and water in a jug; season.
4 Arrange tomato and zucchini in base of pan; pour over egg mixture, sprinkle with cottage cheese. Bake for 45 minutes or until set.
5 Meanwhile, combine mesclun and parsley with juice and garlic, toss gently. Serve salad with tart.

The tart can be made ahead and frozen. Defrost overnight in the fridge; warm in a slow oven then top with cottage cheese.

crab and zucchini 'spaghetti'

PREP + COOK TIME 10 MINUTES • SERVES 1

1 medium zucchini (120g)

85g (3 ounces) fresh crab meat

1 fresh long red chilli, chopped finely

¼ teaspoon finely grated lemon rind

1 tablespoon lemon juice

2 teaspoons extra virgin olive oil

1 trimmed celery stick (100g), sliced thinly diagonally

½ cup (20g) firmly packed trimmed watercress

1 Using a mandoline or V-slicer, thinly slice zucchini lengthways, then slice lengthways into long thin strips.

2 Combine zucchini strips and remaining ingredients in a medium bowl; season to taste.

Test Kitchen NOTES

You can use 100g (3 ounces) cooked shredded chicken breast instead of the crab. If you prefer a milder heat, remove the membranes and seeds from the chilli. To check the heat of a chilli, try tasting a chilli seed on its own before cooking. Use a celery stick from the centre of a bunch for a sweeter flavour. Using one green zucchini and one yellow zucchini will give this dish extra colour. If you have one, use a julienne peeler to slice the zucchini into thin strips.

NUTRITIONAL COUNT PER SERVING

▶ 10.2g total fat

▶ 1.6g saturated fat

▶ 777kJ (186 cal)

▶ 6.5g carbohydrate

▶ 15.1g protein

▶ 4.6g fibre

sweet spiced lamb with warm apple and brussels sprouts

PREP + COOK TIME 25 MINUTES • SERVES 1

100g (3 ounces) brussels sprouts, sliced thinly

70g (2½ ounces) lamb loin

½ clove garlic, crushed

¼ teaspoon ground cinnamon

½ teaspoon each ground cumin and coriander

½ small red onion (50g), sliced thinly

1 small apple (100g), sliced thinly into rounds

1 tablespoon fat-free natural yoghurt

1 Place sprouts in a medium heatproof bowl; cover with boiling water. Stand for 30 seconds, then drain. Plunge sprouts into a large bowl filled with iced water to refresh; drain.

2 Rub lamb with combined garlic, and spices; season. Cook lamb on a heated oiled grill plate (or grill or barbecue) for 3 minutes, turning halfway through cooking time, or until cooked as desired. Stand, covered, for 5 minutes.

3 Cook onion and apple on grill plate until browned lightly and softened.

4 Combine sprouts, onion and apple in a medium bowl; toss well.

5 Serve salad with lamb; accompany with yoghurt.

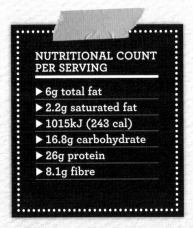

NUTRITIONAL COUNT PER SERVING

▶ 6g total fat
▶ 2.2g saturated fat
▶ 1015kJ (243 cal)
▶ 16.8g carbohydrate
▶ 26g protein
▶ 8.1g fibre

Swap the lamb for chicken, pork or beef, if you prefer; choose lean cuts of meat.

thai crab fritters with cabbage salad

150g (4½ ounces) fresh crab meat

1 egg white, beaten lightly

3 teaspoons cornflour (cornstarch)

1 teaspoon kecap manis

1 green onion (scallion), sliced thinly

1 teaspoon finely chopped fresh mint

1 teaspoon finely chopped fresh coriander (cilantro)

2 lime wedges

CABBAGE SALAD

40g (1½ ounces) snow peas, sliced thinly lengthways

50g (1½ ounces) wombok (napa cabbage), sliced thinly

20g (¾ ounce) baby spinach leaves, shredded finely

¼ small red capsicum (bell pepper) (35g), sliced thinly

½ lebanese cucumber (65g), cut lengthways into ribbons, then sliced lengthways into thin strips

2 teaspoons thinly sliced fresh mint

2 teaspoons thinly sliced fresh coriander (cilantro)

1 tablespoon fried noodle salad dressing

2 teaspoons lime juice

1 Combine crab, egg white, cornflour, kecap manis, onion and herbs in a small bowl; season.

2 Make cabbage salad.

3 Heat a medium non-stick frying pan over medium heat; cook rounded tablespoons of crab mixture for 2 minutes each side or until fritters are browned and cooked through.

4 Serve fritters with cabbage salad and lime wedges.

CABBAGE SALAD Combine ingredients in a large bowl; toss gently. Season to taste.

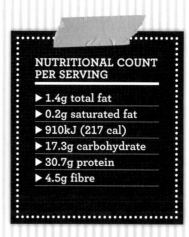

NUTRITIONAL COUNT PER SERVING

▶ 1.4g total fat
▶ 0.2g saturated fat
▶ 910kJ (217 cal)
▶ 17.3g carbohydrate
▶ 30.7g protein
▶ 4.5g fibre

Test Kitchen
NOTES

Use any asian-style dressing
you like. You can swap the
crab meat with shredded
barbecue chicken breast.
If you are having trouble
purchasing fresh crab meat,
used drained, canned crab
meat, instead. If you have one,
use a julienne peeler to slice
the cucumber into thin strips.

baked curry fish with broccolini

NUTRITIONAL COUNT PER SERVING

▶ 3.7g total fat
▶ 0.8g saturated fat
▶ 1298kJ (310 cal)
▶ 40.6g carbohydrate
▶ 25g protein
▶ 5.6g fibre

¼ cup (50g) brown rice

½ cup (125ml) water

150g (4½ ounces) broccolini, sliced thinly

100g (3 ounces) skinless firm white fish fillet

½ teaspoon curry powder

¼ cup (60ml) chicken stock

1 tablespoon fresh coriander leaves (cilantro)

1 tablespoon fat-free natural yoghurt

1 lemon wedge

1 Place rice and the water in a small saucepan; bring to the boil. Reduce heat; cook, covered, for 25 minutes or until tender.
2 Meanwhile, preheat oven to 220°C/425°F.
3 Place broccolini in a small ovenproof dish.
4 Score fish lightly with a small, sharp knife. Rub curry powder all over fish, season. Place fish on top of broccolini, pour over stock.
5 Transfer to oven; cook, uncovered, for 8 minutes or until cooked through.
6 Serve fish and broccolini with rice, coriander, yoghurt and lemon. Spoon over pan juices.

To speed things up, use microwave brown rice.

lentil and beetroot salad

⅓ cup (50g) canned lentils, rinsed, drained

1 baby fennel bulb (130g), sliced thinly

½ lebanese cucumber (65g), cut lengthways into ribbons, then sliced lengthways into thin strips

100g (3 ounces) canned baby beetroot (beet), quartered

¼ cup firmly packed fresh mint leaves

2 cups (120g) firmly packed watercress leaves

1 tablespoon fat-free balsamic vinaigrette

1 Combine lentils, fennel, cucumber, beetroot, mint and watercress in a large bowl.
2 Just before serving; drizzle with dressing; season to taste.

Test Kitchen NOTES

Swap watercress with rocket (arugula), if you like, or use another slightly bitter leafy green vegetable. Fresh beetroot is delicious roasted and tossed through the salad instead of the canned variety. If you have one, use a julienne peeler to slice the cucumber into thin strips.

NUTRITIONAL COUNT PER SERVING

▶ 8.2g total fat
▶ 0.8g saturated fat
▶ 1240kJ (296 cal)
▶ 32.8g carbohydrate
▶ 15.4g protein
▶ 16.1g fibre

asian tofu omelette wrap

PREP + COOK TIME 20 MINUTES • SERVES 1

1 egg

2 teaspoons water

70g (2½ ounces) gai lan

100g (3 ounces) firm tofu, crumbled coarsely

½ fresh long red chilli, sliced thinly

1 clove garlic, crushed

2 teaspoons finely grated fresh ginger

½ small carrot (35g), cut into long matchsticks

1 green onion (scallion), sliced thinly lengthways

2 teaspoons light soy sauce

1 tablespoon water, extra

2 teaspoons sweet chilli sauce

1 Whisk egg and the water together in a small bowl; season. Cut gai lan stalks into 2cm (¾-inch) pieces; coarsely chop leaves.

2 Heat a lightly oiled small non-stick frying pan over medium heat. Pour egg mixture into pan; swirl to coat base of pan. Cook for 2 minutes, without stirring, or until cooked through. Gently turn egg onto a plate; cover to keep warm.

3 Increase heat to high; cook tofu, chilli, garlic and ginger in pan, stirring, for 2 minutes or until tofu is browned. Remove from pan; cover to keep warm.

4 Cook carrot, gai lan stalks, green onion, soy sauce and the extra water in pan, stirring, for 2 minutes or until gai lan is tender. Stir in gai lan leaves; cook, for 30 seconds or until just wilted.

5 Top half the omelette with tofu and vegetables; fold over to enclose. Drizzle with sweet chilli sauce to serve.

NUTRITIONAL COUNT PER SERVING

▶ 12.6g total fat
▶ 2.7g saturated fat
▶ 1033kJ (247 cal)
▶ 5.9g carbohydrate
▶ 21.9g protein
▶ 11.9g fibre

If you have one, use a julienne peeler to slice the carrot into thin strips.

pumpkin and zucchini tagine

¼ teaspoon ground cinnamon

½ teaspoon each ground ginger, cumin and sweet paprika

100g (3 ounces) butternut pumpkin, cut into 3cm (1¼-inch) pieces

½ small red onion (40g), cut into wedges

1 cup (250ml) chicken stock

1 medium zucchini (120g), sliced thickly diagonally

¼ cup (50g) couscous

¼ cup (60ml) boiling water

2 teaspoons finely chopped preserved lemon rind

⅓ cup fresh coriander leaves (cilantro)

1 Heat a lightly oiled medium saucepan over medium heat; cook cinnamon, ginger, cumin and paprika for 30 seconds or until fragrant.

2 Add pumpkin, onion and stock to pan; bring to a simmer. Cook, covered, for 10 minutes or until pumpkin is tender. Add zucchini; cook for 2 minutes. Season to taste.

3 Meanwhile, combine couscous with the boiling water in a medium heatproof bowl, cover; stand for 5 minutes or until water is absorbed, fluffing with a fork occasionally. Add lemon and half the coriander.

4 Serve tagine with couscous; sprinkle with the remaining coriander.

NUTRITIONAL COUNT PER SERVING

▶ 2.9g total fat
▶ 0.4g saturated fat
▶ 1215kJ (290 cal)
▶ 50.5g carbohydrate
▶ 10.9g protein
▶ 8.5g fibre

Add baby mint leaves for extra flavour.

one-pot poached chicken with soba noodles

PREP + COOK TIME 25 MINUTES • SERVES 1

3 cups (750ml) water

20g (¾ ounce) piece fresh ginger, peeled, sliced thinly

100g (3 ounces) chicken breast fillet

30g (1 ounce) soba noodles

¼ cup (50g) frozen shelled green soya beans (edamame)

80g (2½ ounces) rainbow chard leaves, chopped coarsely

1 green onion (scallion), sliced thinly diagonally

1 tablespoon light soy sauce

1 teaspoon honey

3 teaspoons lime juice

½ clove garlic, crushed

1 Fill a medium saucepan with the water, add ginger, bring to the boil; reduce heat to low. Add chicken to pan; simmer for 10 minutes or until chicken is cooked through. Remove chicken and ginger from pan; discard ginger, reserve poaching liquid.

2 Return poaching liquid to the boil. Add noodles; cook for 3 minutes. Add beans and chard to pan; cook for 1 minute. Drain; return noodle mixture to pan.

3 Shred chicken; add to noodle mixture with onion.

4 Combine sauce, honey, juice and garlic in a small bowl; drizzle over noodle mixture to serve.

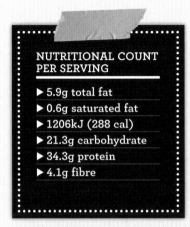

NUTRITIONAL COUNT PER SERVING

▶ 5.9g total fat
▶ 0.6g saturated fat
▶ 1206kJ (288 cal)
▶ 21.3g carbohydrate
▶ 34.3g protein
▶ 4.1g fibre

You can use silver beet or spinach if you
are unable to get rainbow chard.

spicy tuna tabbouleh

PREP + COOK TIME 25 MINUTES • SERVES 1

NUTRITIONAL COUNT PER SERVING

▸ 2.5g total fat
▸ 0.6g saturated fat
▸ 1155kJ (276 cal)
▸ 6.6g carbohydrate
▸ 22.8g protein
▸ 11.6g fibre

40g (1½ ounces) cracked wheat

⅔ cup (160ml) water

1 tablespoon chopped pickled jalapeños

95g (3 ounces) canned tuna in springwater, drained

100g (3 ounces) cherry tomatoes, halved

100g (3 ounces) lebanese cucumber, sliced thickly

2 tablespoons fresh mint leaves

2 tablespoons fresh flat-leaf parsley leaves

1 green onion (scallion), sliced thinly

2 teaspoons lemon juice

1 lemon wedge

1 Place cracked wheat and the water in a small saucepan. Bring to the boil, reduce heat to low; cook, covered, for 15 minutes or until tender. Drain, rinse under cold water until cool; drain.

2 Combine wheat with the remaining ingredients in a medium bowl; season to taste. Serve with lemon.

Test Kitchen NOTES

Make the salad ahead of time, but keep the lemon juice separate until ready to serve. Try this with shredded chicken instead of the tuna. Jalapeños are fairly hot green chillies available in brine, bottled, or fresh from specialty greengrocers; we used bottled jalapeños in this recipe.

zucchini and corn fritters

PREP + COOK TIME 15 MINUTES • SERVES 1

½ small zucchini (50g), chopped finely

½ cup (80g) frozen corn, thawed

1 egg, beaten lightly

olive-oil cooking spray

2 cherry tomatoes, quartered

30g (1 ounce) avocado, chopped coarsely

2 teaspoons lime juice

1 tablespoon coarsely chopped fresh coriander
(cilantro)

1 Combine zucchini, corn and egg in a small bowl;
season.
2 Heat a small non-stick frying pan over medium
heat; spray with oil. Place 2 oiled egg rings in pan.
Divide egg mixture evenly among egg rings; cook
for 2 minutes each side or until golden and cooked
through. Transfer to plate; cover to keep warm.
3 Combine tomato, avocado, juice and coriander
in a small bowl; season to taste. Serve tomato salad
with fritters.

You can use drained, canned corn instead of the frozen corn, or replace the corn with peas or peeled, mashed broad beans.

**NUTRITIONAL COUNT
PER SERVING**

▸ 14.1g total fat
▸ 3.5g saturated fat
▸ 1006kJ (240 cal)
▸ 15.7g carbohydrate
▸ 10.6g protein
▸ 4g fibre

tuna carpaccio
with asian salad

NUTRITIONAL COUNT PER SERVING

▶ 4.5g total fat
▶ 0.7g saturated fat
▶ 770kJ (184 cal)
▶ 7.1g carbohydrate
▶ 25.5g protein
▶ 4.2g fibre

tuna carpaccio with asian salad

80g (2½ ounces) tuna steak

50g (1½ ounces) red cabbage, shredded finely

20g (¾ ounce) curly endive (frisee lettuce)

½ baby fennel bulb (65g), sliced thinly

½ lebanese cucumber (65g), cut into ribbons

1 teaspoon sesame seeds, lightly toasted

WASABI DRESSING

1 teaspoon kecap manis

1 tablespoon lime juice

½ teaspoon wasabi

½ teaspoon mirin

¼ teaspoon sesame oil

1 Heat a lightly oiled small frying pan over high heat; cook tuna for 1 minute each side or until golden. Transfer to a plate; cool. Cover; refrigerate for 10 minutes.
2 Meanwhile, combine cabbage, lettuce, fennel and cucumber in a small bowl.
3 Make wasabi dressing.
4 Slice tuna thickly; arrange over salad. Drizzle with dressing; serve sprinkled with sesame seeds.

WASABI DRESSING Combine ingredients in a screw-top jar; shake well.

char-grilled chicken with sauteed kale

125g (4 ounces) chicken breast fillet, trimmed, halved lengthways

1 teaspoon sumac

½ small red onion (50g), sliced thinly

80g (2½ ounces) kale, trimmed, shredded finely

¼ cup (60ml) vegetable stock

2 teaspoons red wine vinegar

20g (¾ ounce) reduced-fat fetta

1 lemon wedge, to serve

1 Sprinkle chicken with sumac; season. Cook chicken on a heated oiled grill plate (or grill or barbecue) for 4 minutes each side or until cooked through.
2 Meanwhile, heat a medium wok over high heat; stir-fry onion for 2 minutes or until softened. Add kale to wok; stir-fry for 1 minute or until wilted. Add stock and vinegar to wok; simmer, uncovered, until kale is tender.
3 Serve kale topped with chicken; sprinkle with fetta, accompany with lemon wedge.

Photograph page 88

NUTRITIONAL COUNT PER SERVING

▶ 5.8g total fat
▶ 2.6g saturated fat
▶ 950kJ (227 cal)
▶ 5.6g carbohydrate
▶ 36g protein
▶ 3g fibre

We used curly kale for this
recipe but cavolo nero (tuscan
cabbage) is also fine. If kale
is unavailable you can use
silver beet, but cook for slightly
less time. For a vegetarian
option, replace the chicken
with field mushrooms.

char-grilled chicken with
sauteed kale, recipe page 87

summer minestrone,
recipe page 90

summer minestrone

1 teaspoon olive oil

1 slice prosciutto (15g), sliced thinly

½ small leek (100g), sliced thinly

½ zucchini (50g), chopped finely

1 clove garlic, crushed

1 cup (250ml) chicken stock

¾ cup (180ml) water

¼ cup (35g) farfalle (bow tie) pasta

¼ cup (30g) frozen peas

½ bunch asparagus (85g), trimmed,
sliced thinly diagonally

1 Heat oil in a small saucepan over medium heat;
cook prosciutto, leek, zucchini and garlic, stirring,
for 2 minutes or until leek softens.
2 Add stock, the water and pasta to pan; bring to
the boil. Reduce heat to low; cook for 8 minutes
or until pasta is tender.
3 Add peas and asparagus; cook for 2 minutes or
until tender. Season to taste.

Photograph page 89

Test Kitchen
NOTE
You can replace the zucchini
with 1 yellow squash, sliced
thinly, and the asparagus with
the same weight of snow peas.

chicken and cashew stir-fry

100g (3 ounces) chicken breast fillet, sliced thinly

¼ teaspoon chinese five-spice powder

olive-oil cooking spray

175g (5½ ounces) broccolini, cut into 5cm (2-inch)
lengths diagonally

½ bunch baby choy sum (150g), ends trimmed

1 tablespoon oyster sauce

2 teaspoons chinese black vinegar

1 tablespoon toasted cashews

1 Combine chicken and spice in a small bowl.
Lightly spray a wok with oil; heat over high heat.
Add chicken; stir-fry, for 2 minutes or until almost
cooked through.
2 Add broccolini; stir-fry for 2 minutes or until just
tender. Add choy sum, sauce, vinegar and nuts;
stir-fry for 1 minute or until choy sum just wilts.

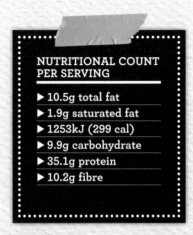

**NUTRITIONAL COUNT
PER SERVING**
► 10.5g total fat
► 1.9g saturated fat
► 1253kJ (299 cal)
► 9.9g carbohydrate
► 35.1g protein
► 10.2g fibre

chicken and cashew stir-fry

Test Kitchen
NOTES

You can replace the choy sum with buk choy and the broccolini with asparagus. Chinese black vinegar can be replaced with balsamic vinegar – you could sweeten it slightly with rice vinegar or mirin.

lentil and carrot soup

PREP + COOK TIME 25 MINUTES • SERVES 1

¼ small brown onion (20g), chopped finely

½ teaspoon ground cumin

¼ teaspoon each ground coriander, turmeric and smoked paprika

½ cup (50g) red lentils

1 medium carrot (120g), chopped coarsely

½ cup (125ml) chicken stock

1 cup (250ml) water

2 mini pappadums (8g)

1 tablespoon no-fat greek yoghurt

1 tablespoon finely chopped fresh mint

1 Heat a small oiled saucepan over medium heat; cook onion and spices, stirring, for 1 minute or until fragrant. Add lentils, carrot, stock and the water; bring to the boil. Reduce heat to low; cook, covered, for 15 minutes or until lentils and carrot are tender.

2 Stand lentil mixture for 10 minutes, then blend or process lentil mixture until smooth. Season to taste.

3 Meanwhile, cook pappadums according to packet directions.

4 Combine yoghurt and mint in a small bowl. Top soup with mint yoghurt; accompany with pappadums.

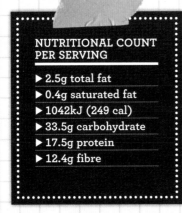

NUTRITIONAL COUNT PER SERVING

▶ 2.5g total fat
▶ 0.4g saturated fat
▶ 1042kJ (249 cal)
▶ 33.5g carbohydrate
▶ 17.5g protein
▶ 12.4g fibre

You can replace the carrot with kumara (orange sweet potato). Sprinkle the soup with ¼ teaspoon of finely chopped lime rind, to serve, if you like.

spice lamb skewers on fattoush

**NUTRITIONAL COUNT
PER SERVING**

▸ 15.2g total fat
▸ 5.6g saturated fat
▸ 1269kJ (303 cal)
▸ 15.4g carbohydrate
▸ 24.9g protein
▸ 3.7g fibre

100g (3 ounces) lamb (ground) mince

¼ teaspoon each ground allspice, cinnamon and cumin

¼ wholemeal pitta pocket (20g)

pinch of sumac

½ lebanese cucumber (65g), sliced thinly

4 cherry tomatoes, halved

¼ cup fresh small mint leaves

1 lemon wedge

1 Combine lamb and spices in a small bowl; season. Shape mixture around two metal skewers.
2 Heat an oiled grill pan (or grill or barbecue) over high heat; cook lamb for 2 minutes each side or until cooked through. Transfer to a plate, cover, keep warm.
3 Sprinkle pitta bread with sumac. Toast on grill pan for 30 seconds each side or until toasted. Break bread into large pieces. Place in a medium bowl with cucumber, tomato and mint; toss to combine. Serve salad with lamb and lemon.

*You can replace the lamb
mince with lean beef mince
or turkey mince.*

grilled cos lettuce with fish

olive-oil cooking spray

150g (4½ ounces) firm white fish fillets

¼ baby cos lettuce (30g), quartered lengthways

170g (5½ ounces) asparagus, trimmed

½ lemon (70g), cut into wedges

2 teaspoons lemon juice

½ teaspoon soy sauce

½ teaspoon honey

1 teaspoon toasted sesame seeds

1 Heat a grill pan (or grill or barbecue) over high heat. Lightly spray fish, lettuce and asparagus with oil; season.

2 Cook fish for 3 minutes each side or until just cooked through.

3 Cook lettuce for 30 seconds each side or until lightly charred. Transfer to a serving plate. Cook asparagus and wedges for 2 minutes or until tender.

4 Meanwhile, combine juice, sauce and honey in a small jug.

5 Serve fish with lettuce, asparagus and lemon; drizzle with dressing, sprinkle with sesame seeds.

Test Kitchen NOTES

You can replace the fish with chicken tenderloins. We used barramundi in this recipe, whiting would also be a suitable fish to use.

NUTRITIONAL COUNT PER SERVING

- ▶ 7.1g total fat
- ▶ 1.3g saturated fat
- ▶ 1006kJ (240 cal)
- ▶ 5.6g carbohydrate
- ▶ 34.5g protein
- ▶ 4.2g fibre

chicken pot au feu
with garlic mashed potato

100g (3 ounces) chicken breast fillet

1 baby carrot (70g), trimmed

1 trimmed celery stick (100g), cut into 4cm (1½ inch) lengths

1 small brown onion (80g), halved

1 clove garlic, peeled

1 cup (250ml) chicken stock

½ cup (125ml) water

1 small potato (120g)

2 teaspoons skim milk

2 teaspoons wholegrain mustard

1 tablespoon fresh flat-leaf parsley leaves

1 Combine chicken, carrot, celery, onion, garlic, stock and the water in a medium saucepan, season; bring to the boil. Reduce heat to low; simmer, covered, for 10 minutes or until the chicken is cooked through and vegetables are tender.

2 Remove chicken and vegetables from stock to a bowl; cover to keep warm. Reserve 2 tablespoons of the stock (either freeze the remaining stock in an airtight container for another use or discard).

3 Meanwhile, boil, steam or microwave potato until tender. Mash potato in a medium bowl along with the garlic (from the cooked vegetables) and milk; season to taste.

4 Slice chicken; serve with garlic potato, vegetables, mustard and reserved stock; sprinkle with parsley.

NUTRITIONAL COUNT PER SERVING

► 2.6g total fat
► 0.6g saturated fat
► 1107kJ (264 cal)
► 25.8g carbohydrate
► 29.1g protein
► 9.2g fibre

Cook the potato in the left over stock to add more flavour to the mash; add extra water if there is not enough stock to cover the potato.

apricot and mint stuffed pork with rocket, mint and radish salad

1 small clove garlic, crushed

½ fresh apricot (25g), chopped finely

2 teaspoons finely chopped fresh mint

5g (¼ ounce) butter, softened

150g (8 ounces) pork loin steak, trimmed

20g (¾ ounce) rocket (arugula)

2 tablespoons fresh small mint leaves, extra

1 small red radish (15g), sliced thinly

2 teaspoons lemon juice

1 Combine garlic, apricot, mint and butter in a small bowl; season.

2 Butterfly the pork chop by slicing in half crossways stopping at the bone; open out and spread one side with the apricot mixture. Enclose the filling, secure with toothpicks (make sure the cutlet can sit flat), season.

3 Cook pork in a heated lightly oiled grill pan (or grill or barbecue) over medium heat for 3 minutes each side or until cooked as desired. Transfer to a plate; stand, covered, for 5 minutes.

4 Meanwhile, combine rocket, extra mint, radish and juice in a small bowl; season to taste.

5 Discard toothpicks; serve pork with salad.

NUTRITIONAL COUNT PER SERVING

▶ 8.1g total fat
▶ 2.8g saturated fat
▶ 894kJ (213 cal)
▶ 2.7g carbohydrate
▶ 30.4g protein
▶ 2.1g fibre

lemon-herbed beef
with kale and asparagus

PREP + COOK TIME 10 MINUTES (+ REFRIGERATION) • SERVES 1

1 teaspoon olive oil

¼ teaspoon finely grated lemon rind

1 small clove garlic, crushed

2 tablespoons coarsely chopped
fresh flat-leaf parsley

1 tablespoon coarsely chopped fresh oregano

125g (4 ounces) beef minute steak, trimmed

3 teaspoons lemon juice

30g (1 ounces) kale leaves, torn

2 teaspoons water

85g (3 ounces) asparagus, trimmed

strips of lemon rind, to serve

1 Combine oil, rind, garlic and half each of the parsley and oregano in a shallow dish; add beef, toss to combine in marinade. Cover; refrigerate for 2 hours or overnight.

2 Cook beef in a heated lightly oiled grill pan (or grill or barbecue) for 30 seconds each side or until cooked as desired. Transfer beef to a clean shallow dish with the remaining herbs and juice; cover, stand for 10 minutes.

3 Meanwhile, place kale and the water on a 30cm x 35cm (12-inch x 14-inch) piece of foil; fold foil to enclose kale. Cook kale and asparagus in a heated grill pan (or grill or barbecue) for 2 minutes or until just tender.

4 Serve steak with kale and asparagus.

NUTRITIONAL COUNT
PER SERVING

▶ 12.4g total fat
▶ 3.7g saturated fat
▶ 1045kJ (250 cal)
▶ 2.7g carbohydrate
▶ 29.8g protein
▶ 4g fibre

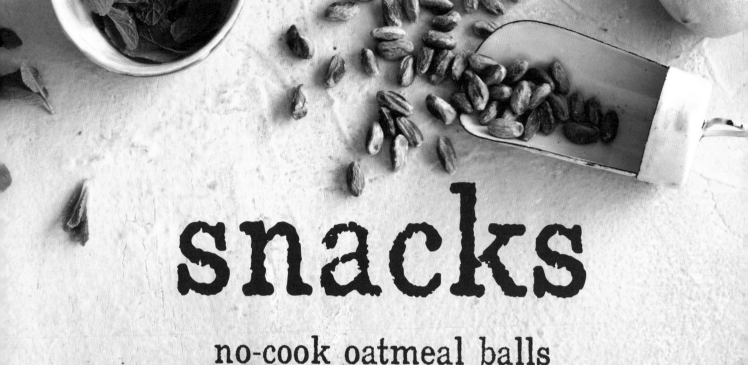

snacks

no-cook oatmeal balls

PREP TIME 10 MINUTES (+ REFRIGERATION) • MAKES ABOUT 22

1 cup oat bran (120g)

½ cup light peanut butter (140g)

⅓ cup linseeds (65g)

1 cup desiccated coconut (80g)

⅓ cup honey (115g)

¼ cup (60ml) water

1 teaspoon vanilla extract

1 Combine ingredients in a large bowl; refrigerate for 30 minutes.

2 Using damp hands, roll heaped tablespoons of the mixture into balls. Refrigerate or freeze until firm.

NUTRITIONAL COUNT PER SERVING

▶ 6g total fat
▶ 2.5g saturated fat
▶ 438kJ (104 cal)
▶ 9.7g carbohydrate
▶ 2.6g protein
▶ 2.7g fibre

Test Kitchen
NOTES

You can make these ahead of
time and store them in the
fridge for up to 2 weeks, or
freeze for up to 3 months.
This has double the amount
of calories for a snack but is
great as a breakfast snack or,
if you prefer to skip breakfast,
to have as a mid-morning
snack. Make sure you adjust
your other meals to stay
within the allowed calories
for the day.

BITES

choc-honey balls

PREP TIME 10 MINUTES (+ REFRIGERATION)
MAKES 10 (1 BALL PER SERVE)

Blend ½ cup All-Bran and ¼ cup roasted walnuts until finely ground. Combine with ⅓ cup finely chopped dried apricots, 1 tablespoon honey, 2 teaspoons water and 2 teaspoons dutch cocoa powder in a bowl. Roll level tablespoons of mixture into balls; refrigerate for 1 hour or until firm.

nutritional count per ball 1.9g total fat (0.2g saturated fat); 206kJ (49 cal); 6.3g carbohydrate; 1.1g protein; 1.6g fibre

Store remaining balls in an airtight container in the refrigerator for up to 2 weeks.

raw hazelnut brownie

PREP TIME 15 MINUTES (+REFRIGERATION)
MAKES 20 (1 BALL PER SERVE)

Process ½ cup roasted pecans, ¼ cup cocoa powder and 2 tablespoons ground hazelnuts until finely chopped. While motor is operating, add ⅔ cup dates in 3 batches; process until mixture resembles coarse crumbs. Roll 2 level teaspoons of mixture into balls. Refrigerate for 1 hour or until firm.

nutritional count per ball 2.8g total fat (0.3g saturated fat); 180kJ (43 cal); 3.4g carbohydrate; 0.7g protein; 1.1g fibre

roasted pumpkin seed spiced trail mix

PREP TIME 5 MINUTES (+ COOLING)
SERVES 6 (1 TABLESPOON PER SERVE)

Dry-fry 2 tablespoons each of pepitas and almonds, and 1½ tablespoons rolled rye in a small non-stick frying pan over medium heat; cook, stirring, for 2 minutes or until browned lightly. Transfer to a small bowl; cool. Stir in a pinch each of chilli powder and sea salt.

nutritional count per serve 3.6g total fat (0.4g saturated fat); 207kJ (49 cal); 2.1g carbohydrate; 1.6g protein; 0.7g fibre

Store remaining trail mix in an airtight container for up to 2 weeks, or in the refrigerator for up to 2 months.

coconut pistachio bites

PREP + COOK TIME 45 MINUTES (+ REFRIGERATION)
MAKES 24 (1 BITE PER SERVE)

Preheat oven to 140°C/300°F. Grease two 12-hole (1-tablespoon/20ml) mini muffin pans. Process ¼ cup coconut flakes, 2 tablespoons chopped pistachios and 1½ cups All-Bran until coarsely ground; transfer to a medium bowl. Stir in 2 tablespoons each of light agave syrup and coconut oil until combined. Divide mixture firmly into pan holes. Bake for 25 minutes or until firm; cool. Refrigerate for 2 hours or until cold. Carefully remove bites from pan with a palette knife.

nutritional count per bite 40.6g total fat (2.6g saturated fat); 170kJ (41 cal); 2.9g carbohydrate; 0.7g protein; 1.3g fibre

Store remaining bites in an airtight container in the fridge for up to 1 month.

Healthy DIPS

creamy spinach dip

PREP + COOK 10 MINUTES • SERVES 1

Boil, steam or microwave 30g (1oz) baby
spinach until wilted; squeeze out excess
water, finely chop. Combine chopped
spinach, 2 tablespoons no-fat plain yoghurt,
¼ teaspoon finely grated lemon rind and
1 teaspoon lemon juice in a small bowl;
season to taste. Serve dip with 2 baby
red radishes, cut into small wedges.

nutritional count per serve 0.4g total fat
(0.2g saturated fat); 202kJ (48 cal);
6.8g carbohydrate; 3.5g protein; 1g fibre

Dip can be served with baby carrots or celery.

cottage cheese and tuna dip

PREP 10 MINUTES • SERVES 1

Combine 2 tablespoons drained canned reduced-
fat tuna in springwater and 2 teaspoons reduced-
fat cottage cheese in a small bowl; season to taste.
Stir through 2 teaspoons thinly sliced fresh
coriander leaves (cilantro). Serve with 2 snow peas,
halved lengthways.

nutritional count per serve 1.4g total fat (0.6g saturated fat);
223kJ (53 cal); 0.6g carbohydrate; 9.5g protein; 0.3g fibre

Store remaining tuna, covered, in the fridge to have on a
non-fasting day. Dip may be served with sugar snap peas.

spiced pumpkin dip

PREP + COOK 10 MINUTES • SERVES 1

Boil, steam or microwave 80g (2½oz) coarsely chopped pumpkin; drain well. Mash pumpkin in a small bowl with a fork until smooth. Stir in ½ small crushed garlic clove and ¼ teaspoon each ground coriander and cumin; season to taste. Serve dip with half a lebanese cucumber, sliced thickly diagonally.

nutritional count per serve 0.5g total fat (0g saturated fat); 211kJ (50 cal); 8.2g carbohydrate; 1.8g protein; 3.1g fibre

Swap pumpkin for kumara (orange sweet potato). Sprinkle with cumin seeds to serve, if you like.

spicy eggplant dip

PREP + COOK 10 MINUTES • SERVES 1

Boil, steam or microwave 1 finger eggplant until tender; chop finely. Combine in a small bowl with 1 tablespoon no-fat greek yoghurt and a pinch each of ground chilli and cumin; season to taste. Top with ¼ teaspoon toasted sesame seeds. Serve dip with 60g (2oz) celery, cut diagonally into batons.

nutritional count per serve 0.9g total fat (0.1g saturated fat); 186kJ (44 cal); 5g carbohydrate; 2.4g protein; 2.7g fibre

DRINKS

gazpacho juice

PREP TIME 5 MINUTES · SERVES 2

Blend or process 2 medium chopped tomatoes,
½ small chopped capsicum (bell pepper), ½ small
chopped cucumber, 1 chopped green onion
(scallion), 2 teaspoons chopped fresh basil leaves
and ½ teaspoon rice vinegar until smooth.

nutritional count per serve 0.3g total fat (0g saturated fat);
175kJ (42 cal); 5.7g carbohydrate; 2.3g protein; 2.9g fibre

Store the remaining juice in the fridge overnight. You
could have this whole recipe as a meal for breakfast.

strawberry and watermelon juice

PREP TIME 5 MINUTES · SERVES 1

Blend 125g (4oz) hulled strawberries and
75g (2½oz) chopped watermelon until smooth.

nutritional count per serve 0.4g total fat
(0g saturated fat); 210kJ (50 cal);
8.2g carbohydrate; 2.4g protein; 2.2g fibre

Freeze the watermelon for an icy cold snack.

iced lemon & mint green tea

PREP TIME 5 MINUTES (+ REFRIGERATION) SERVES 1

Combine 1 green tea bag, 1 cup hot water and ¼ teaspoon finely grated lemon rind in a small jug. Refrigerate for 1 hour or until cold. Stir in 2 teaspoons lemon juice and 1 tablespoon fresh mint leaves; lightly bruise the mint leaves in the tea using the end of a rolling pin or wooden spoon. Stir in ice cubes to serve.

nutritional count per serve 0.2g total fat (0.2g saturated fat); 184kJ (44 cal); 9.3g carbohydrate; 1.2g protein; 0.3g fibre

cucumber, lime & coconut water

PREP TIME 5 MINUTES • SERVES 1

Push 30g (1oz) cucumber through a juice extractor into a glass. Stir through ¾ cup coconut water and 2 teaspoons lime juice. Stir in ice and top with a small sprig of fresh mint.

nutritional count per serve 0.2g total fat (0.2g saturated fat); 184kJ (44 cal); 9.3g carbohydrate; 1.2g protein; 0.3g fibre

You can use fresh coconut juice from a young coconut, if you like.

Calorie COUNTER

All Bran (100g/3 ounces)	1331kJ (318 cal)	Carrot, 1 medium (120g/4 ounces)	138kJ (33 cal)	Egg white, large (32g/1 ounce)	63kJ (15 cal)
Asparagus (100g/3 ounces)	88kJ (21 cal)	Cashews, roasted, unsalted, 1 tablespoon	293kJ (70 cal)	Eggplant, 1 medium (300g/9½ ounces)	268kJ (64 cal)
Apple, 1 medium (150g/4½ ounces)	305kJ (73 cal)	Cauliflower (100g/3 ounces)	100kJ (24 cal)	Fish, firm white fillet (100g/3 ounces)	334kJ (80 cal)
Avocado, 1 small (200g/6½ ounces)	1292kJ (309 cal)	Celery, 1 stalk (100g/3 ounces)	50kJ (12 cal)	Gai lan (100g/3 ounces)	117kJ (28 cal)
Banana, 1 medium (200g/6½ ounces)	527kJ (126 cal)	Cheese, cottage, low fat, 1 tablespoon	92kJ (22 cal)	Garlic, 1 clove	13kJ (3 cal)
Beans, baked (100g/3 ounces)	324kJ (77 cal)	Cheese, parmesan, shaved/grated, 1 tablespoon	113kJ (27 cal)	Ginger, grated, 1 teaspoon	4kJ (1 cal)
Beef, fillet (100g/3 ounces)	1179kJ (282 cal)	Cheese, ricotta, low-fat, 1 tablespoon	92kJ (22 cal)	Grapes (125g/4 ounces)	364kJ (87 cal)
Beef, minced (ground), lean (100g/3 ounces)	761kJ (182 cal)	Chicken, breast, lean (100g/3 ounces)	439kJ (105 cal)	Herbs, fresh, chopped, 1 teaspoon	0kJ (0 cal)
Beef, roast, rare, deli-sliced, 1 slice (15g/½ ounce)	67kJ (16 cal)	Chickpeas, canned, drained (125g/4 ounces)	410kJ (98 cal)	Honey, 1 teaspoon	96kJ (23 cal)
Beef, rump (100g/3 ounces)	907kJ (217 cal)	Ciabatta, bread, 1 slice (35g/1 ounce)	426kJ (102 cal)	Honeydew melon (100g/3 ounces)	149kJ (36 cal)
Blueberries (125g/4 ounces)	242kJ (58 cal)	Coconut, dessicated/ flaked, 1 teaspoon	42kJ (10 cal)	Horseradish cream, 1 teaspoon	38kJ (9 cal)
Bread, rye, 1 slice (45g/1½ ounces)	477kJ (114 cal)	Coconut milk, light, 1 cup (250ml)	740kJ (177 cal)	Jam, diet (low-calorie), 1 teaspoon	4kJ (1 cal)
Bread, wholemeal, 1 slice (45g/1½ ounces)	441kJ (105 cal)	Consomme, beef, 1 cup (250ml)	205kJ (49 cal)	Juice, apple, 1 cup (250ml)	468kJ (112 cal)
Broccoli (100g/3 ounces)	125kJ (30 cal)	Corn thins, 1 piece (6g/¼ ounce)	88kJ (21 cal)	Juice, orange, 1 cup (250ml)	472kJ (113 cal)
Broccolini (100g/3 ounces)	125kJ (30 cal)	Cranberries, fresh/frozen (125g/4 ounces)	242kJ (58 cal)	Kale, raw (100g/3 ounces)	90kJ (22 cal)
Buk choy (100g/3 ounces)	117kJ (28 cal)	Cucumber, lebanese, 1 (130g/4 ounces)	67kJ (16 cal)	Kumara (orange sweet potato) (100g/3 ounces)	314kJ (75 cal)
Capsicum (bell pepper), 1 medium (200g/6½ ounces)	171kJ (41 cal)	Dressing, salad, oil-free, 1 tablespoon	29kJ (7 cal)	Leek, 1 medium (350g/11 ounces)	217kJ (52 cal)
Capsicum (bell pepper), char-grilled, drained (100g/3 ounces)	355kJ (85 cal)	Egg, whole, large (59g/2 ounces)	288kJ (69 cal)	Lettuce, cos (romaine) (100g/3 ounces)	50kJ (12 cal)

Margarine, low-fat, 1 teaspoon	54kJ (13 cal)	Pork fillet (100g/3 ounces)	418kJ (100 cal)	Stock, fish, 1 cup (250ml)	100kJ (24 cal)
Milk, almond 1 cup (250ml)	71kJ (17 cal)	Potato, 1 medium (200g/6½ ounces)	431kJ (103 cal)	Stock, vegetable, 1 cup (250ml)	100kJ (24 cal)
Milk, skim, 1 cup (250ml)	372kJ (89 cal)	Prawns (shrimp) (100g/3 ounces)	372kJ (89 cal)	Strawberries (125g/4 ounces)	113kJ (27 cal)
Mountain bread wraps, rye, 1 (30g/1 ounce)	322kJ (77 cal)	Prosciutto, 1 slice (15g/½ ounce)	155kJ (37 cal)	Sugar, brown, 1 teaspoon	46kJ (11 cal)
Mushrooms (100g/3 ounces)	105kJ (25 cal)	Pumpkin, peeled (100g/3 ounces)	184kJ (44 cal)	Sugar, caster (superfine), 1 teaspoon	67kJ (16 cal)
Noodles, rice stick (100g/3 ounces)	364kJ (87 cal)	Radicchio, 1 small (150g/4½ ounces)	71kJ (17 cal)	Sugar, icing (confectioners'), 1 teaspoon	46kJ (11 cal)
Oats, rolled (100g/3 ounces)	1572 (376 cal)	Raspberries (125g/4 ounces)	280kJ (67 cal)	Sugar, raw, 1 teaspoon	67kJ (16 cal)
Oil, canola, 1 teaspoon	171kJ (41 cal)	Rice cakes, 1 piece (6g/¼ ounce)	150kJ (36 cal)	Sweetener, artificial (equal etc), 1 teaspoon	8kJ (2 cal)
Oil, canola/cooking-oil spray, 1-second spray	38kJ (9 cal)	Rice, jasmine (½ cup cooked)	464kJ (11 cal)	Tofu, silken (100g/3 ounces)	259 (62 cal)
Oil, olive, regular, 1 teaspoon	167kJ (40 cal)	Rocket (arugula) (100g/3 ounces)	84kJ (20 cal)	Tomato, 1 medium (150g/4½ ounces)	113kJ (27 cal)
Oil, peanut, 1 teaspoon	167kJ (40 cal)	Rockmelon (100g/3 ounces)	121kJ (29 cal)	Tomatoes, roma (egg) truss (250g/8 ounces)	159kJ (38 cal)
Oil, vegetable, 1 teaspoon	171kJ (41 cal)	Salmon, smoked, 1 slice (25g/¾ ounce)	140kJ (34 cal)	Tomatoes, cherry (250g/8 ounces)	159kJ (38 cal)
Olives, 1 tablespoon	125kJ (30 cal)	Sauce, fish, 1 teaspoon	13kJ (3 cal)	Tuna, canned in brine, drained (125g/4 ounces)	619kJ (148 cal)
Onion, brown, 1 medium (150g/4½ ounces)	184kJ (44 cal)	Sauce, oyster, 1 teaspoon	29kJ (7 cal)	Tuna, canned in oil, drained (125g/4 ounces)	1108kJ (265 cal)
Onion, red, 1 medium (170g/5½ ounces)	209kJ (50 cal)	Silver beet (swiss chard), 1 leaf (65g/2 ounces)	46kJ (11 cal)	Tuna, canned in springwater, drained (125g/4 ounces)	619kJ (148 cal)
Onion, green (scallion), 1	13kJ (3 cal)	Snow peas (100g/3 ounces)	150kJ (36 cal)	Turkey, roast, deli, 1 slice (15g/½ ounce)	92kJ (22 cal)
Orange, 1 medium (240g/7½ ounces)	393kJ (94 cal)	Spinach, baby (100g/3 ounces)	84kJ (20 cal)	Watermelon, peeled (100g/3 ounces)	125kJ (30 cal)
Pear, 1 medium (230g/7 ounces)	380kJ (91 cal)	Sprouts, bean (10g/½ ounce)	8kJ (2 cal)	Yoghurt, skim milk, natural, 1 tablespoon	50kJ (12 cal)
Peas, frozen. 1 cup (120g/4 ounces)	330kJ (79 cal)	Stock, beef, 1 cup (250ml)	92kJ (22 cal)	Yoghurt, skim milk, flavoured, 1 tablespoon	63kJ (15 cal)
Popcorn, air-popped, 1 cup (25g/¾ ounce)	359kJ (86 cal)	Stock, chicken, 1 cup (250ml)	79kJ (19 cal)	Zucchini, 1 medium (120g/4 ounces)	71kJ (17 cal)

Cooking TECHNIQUES

preparing asparagus

To snap the woody end off the asparagus, hold it close to the base and bend it until it snaps. Discard the woody end and then trim the asparagus with a vegetable peeler.

crushing garlic

Press garlic firmly with the flat blade of a large knife (top) crushing the clove. Simply pull off the papery skin. A garlic press (bottom) removes and leaves the skin behind while crushing the garlic.

trimming beetroot

To trim beetroot, cut the stems to 2cm (¾ inch) from the bulb. Don't trim the beard at the base of the plant as this stops the colour from bleeding during cooking.

removing corn kernels

Remove the husk (the outer covering) and the silk (the soft silky inner threads), and trim one side of the corn cob so it lies flat. Use a large flat-bladed knife to cut down the cob, close to the core, to remove the kernels.

slicing vegies thinly

Cutting cucumber, zucchini, carrots, etc, into thin ribbons gives long thin, uniform slices. Use a vegetable peeler to do this. Applying more pressure on the peeler gives a thicker slice.

trimming watercress

Use scissors to cut off the roots, then pull the leaves off any thick, woody stems. This peppery green may also be known as 'winter rocket'.

how to chiffonade

Chiffonade is a way of cutting green leaves into long, thin strips. Lay leaves flat on top of each other, then roll up tightly and cut into thin slices.

trimming a green onion

Pull the papery skin towards the root and off the onion. Cut the root end off, then slice the white end of the onion as directed in the recipe. The green end can be used to garnish the dish.

making a thin omelette

To make a thin omelette, lightly whisk the eggs, then pour into a heated lightly-oiled wok (or large frying pan). Tilt the wok to cover the base with the egg; cook until the egg is set.

slicing a chilli

When slicing a chilli, leave it whole. The seeds are the heat source, so if you are intolerant of high heat levels, remove the seeds and membranes, or use less chilli. Don't touch your face after touching chilli as it can burn your eyes and mouth.

slicing fennel

Slicing fennel thinly is easy using a V-slicer or mandoline – simply slide the fennel back and forth across the blade. The adjustable blade is very sharp, so watch your fingers. A guard is supplied, so use it to protect your fingers from any unwanted mishaps.

slicing capsicum

To slice a capsicum, cut the top and bottom off and stand it on one end; slice down removing all the flesh. Remove and discard the seeds and membranes, then slice the flesh.

GLOSSARY

AGAVE SYRUP a sweetener produced from the agave plant in South Africa and Mexico. It is sweeter than sugar, though less viscous, so it dissolves quickly. Agave syrup is sold in light, amber and dark varieties.

ALL-BRAN CEREAL low-fat, high-fibre breakfast cereal based on wheat bran.

BACON, SHORTCUT is a 'half rasher'; the streaky (belly), narrow portion of the rasher has been removed leaving the choice cut eye meat (fat end).

BAKING POWDER a raising agent consisting mainly of two parts cream of tartar to one part bicarbonate of soda (baking soda), which, when combined, lightens the mixture during baking.

BEANS
broad also known as fava, windsor and horse beans; peel fresh and frozen beans twice (discarding the outer long green pod and the beige tough inner shell).
cannellini a small white bean similar in appearance and flavour to other white beans (great northern, navy or haricot). Available dried or canned.
edamame green baby soya beans; available fresh and frozen from major supermarkets and Asian grocery stores.
green also known as french or string beans (although the tough string they once had has generally been bred out of them); this long thin fresh bean is consumed in its entirety once cooked.
kidney medium-sized red or white bean, slightly floury in texture yet sweet in flavour; sold dried or canned.
sprouts also known as bean shoots; tender new growths of assorted beans and seeds. The most readily available are mung bean, soya bean, alfalfa and snow pea sprouts.

BEEF
eye fillet a very tender cut from the area below the rib cage; also known as beef tenderloin.
minute steaks a thinly sliced cut of beef that cooks very quickly. It can be blade, oyster, round or just about any other cut.

BICARBONATE OF SODA also known as baking or carb soda; used as a raising agent in baking.

BLOOD ORANGE a virtually seedless citrus fruit with blood-red rind and flesh; it has a sweet, non-acidic pulp and juice.

BRAN FLAKES made from the outer layer of a cereal, most often the husks of wheat, rice or oats, which are flattened into light, dry flakes.

BREAD
crumpet a thick flat yeasted cake/bread, with a soft porous texture. It is heated and eaten warm; the top of the cake is covered in small holes, which hold the butter and syrup or whatever topping you add. Do not confuse with english muffins; crumpets are more moist, and are not cut in half to toast. They are sold in most supermarkets.
french stick a long, narrow cylindrical loaf. It has a crisp brown crust and light chewy interior. It is also known as french bread, french loaf or baguette.
mountain wraps a soft-textured, thin, flat bread used for sandwiches, or filled and rolled up.
pitta also known as lebanese bread; a wheat-flour pocket bread sold in large, flat pieces that separate into two thin rounds. Also available in small thick pieces called pocket pitta.
sourdough so-named, not because it's sour in taste, although some are, but because it's made by using a 'starter dough', which contains a yeast culture, mixed into flour and water. Part of the resulting dough is then saved to use as the starter dough next time.
tortillas thin, round unleavened bread originating in Mexico. Two kinds are available, one made from wheat flour and the other from corn (maize meal).

BUTTERMILK originally the term given to the slightly sour liquid left after butter was churned from cream, today it is made similarly to yoghurt. Sold alongside fresh milk products in supermarkets; despite the implication of its name, it's low in fat.

BUTTERNUT PUMPKIN (SQUASH) a member of the gourd family. Butternut is pear-shaped with golden skin and orange flesh.

CHEESE
cottage cheese fresh, white, unripened curd cheese with a grainy consistency and a fat content between 5% and 15%.
light cream cheese commonly known as Philadelphia or Philly, a soft cows-milk cheese available as a blend of cottage and cream cheeses with a fat content of 21%.
parmesan also known as parmigiano, a hard, grainy cows-milk cheese. The curd is salted in brine for a month before being aged for up to two years.

CHICKEN
breast fillet is skinned and boned.
tenderloin the small strip of meat under the breast.

CHILLI, JALAPEÑO a fairly hot green chilli; available bottled in brine or fresh from specialty greengrocers.

CINNAMON dried inner bark of the shoots of the cinnamon tree; available in stick (quill) or ground form.

CORIANDER also known as pak chee, cilantro or chinese parsley; bright-green leafy herb with a pungent flavour. Both the stems and roots of coriander are used in cooking; wash well before using. Is also available ground or as seeds; don't substitute these for fresh coriander as the tastes are completely different.

CORNFLOUR (CORNSTARCH) used as a thickening agent.

COUSCOUS a fine, grain-like cereal product made from semolina; a dough of semolina flour and water is sieved then dehydrated to produce minuscule even-sized pellets of couscous. It is rehydrated by steaming, or with the addition of a warm liquid, and swells to three or four times its original size.

CUMIN, GROUND a spice also known as zeera or comino, resembling caraway in size; it has a spicy, nutty flavour.

EGGS some recipes in this book may call for raw or barely cooked eggs; exercise caution if there is a salmonella problem in your area. The risk is greater for those who are pregnant, elderly or very young, and those with impaired immune systems.

FILLO PASTRY (also filo and phyllo); tissue-thin pastry sheets.

FISH

firm white fillets blue eye, bream, ling, flathead, swordfish, whiting, jewfish, snapper or sea perch are all good choices. Check for any small pieces of bone in the fillets and use tweezers to remove them.

salmon has a red-pink firm flesh with few bones, and a moist delicate flavour.

trout a delicately flavoured soft, pink-fleshed fish belonging to the same family as salmon (which can be substituted).

FLOUR

buckwheat is a herb belonging to the same plant family as rhubarb; it is not a cereal, so is gluten-free. It is available as a flour; ground into coarse, medium or fine grains.

plain a general all-purpose flour made from wheat.

self-raising (rising) plain flour sifted with baking powder in the proportion of 1 cup plain (all-purpose) flour to 2 teaspoons baking powder.

wholemeal plain a general all-purpose wholewheat flour milled from the whole wheat grain (bran, germ and endosperm).

GARAM MASALA a blend of spices based on cardamom, cinnamon, cloves, coriander, fennel and cumin, roasted and ground together. Black pepper and chilli can be added for a hotter version.

GINGER, FRESH also known as green or root ginger; is the thick root of a tropical plant. Trim, removing any creases and knobbly pieces, then grate or slice thinly.

pickled paper-thin shavings of ginger are pickled in a mixture of vinegar, sugar and natural colouring. Available from Asian food shops.

GOLDEN SYRUP a by-product of refined sugar cane; pure maple syrup or honey can be substituted.

HARISSA a Moroccan sauce or paste made from dried chillies, cumin, garlic, oil and caraway seeds. The paste, available in a tube, is very hot and should not be used in large amounts; bottled harissa sauce is more mild, but if you're not used to heat, even this may be too hot. From supermarkets and Middle-Eastern grocery stores.

LAMB

backstrap the larger fillet from a row of loin chops or cutlets. Lamb fillet may be substituted, although this cut is a little smaller than the backstrap.

cutlets small, tender rib chop.

LENTILS (red, brown, yellow) dried pulses often identified by and named after their colour.

LETTUCE

butter have small, round, loosely formed heads with soft, buttery-textured leaves ranging from pale green on the outer leaves to pale yellow-green on the inner leaves. Has a sweet flavour.

cos also known as romaine lettuce.

iceberg a heavy, firm round lettuce with tightly packed crisp leaves.

MAPLE SYRUP, PURE a thin syrup distilled from the sap of the maple tree. Maple-flavoured syrup or pancake syrup is not an adequate substitute.

MUSTARD

dijon pale brown, distinctively flavoured, fairly mild tasting french mustard.

wholegrain is also known as seeded mustard. A french-style coarse-grain mustard made from crushed mustard seeds and dijon-style french mustard.

OIL

cooking spray we use a cholesterol-free spray made from canola oil.

olive made from ripened olives. Extra virgin and virgin are the best, while extra light or light refers to taste, not fat levels.

sesame made from roasted, crushed, white sesame seeds.

vegetable sourced from plants.

ONION

brown and white are interchangeable, however, white onions have a more pungent flesh.

green an immature onion picked before the bulb has formed; has a long, bright-green edible stalk. Also known as scallion or, incorrectly, shallot.

red also known as spanish, red spanish or bermuda onion; sweet-flavoured, large, purple-red onion.

PEPITAS dried pumpkin seeds.

PORK, STEAK from the loin, which runs along most of the back.

PRESERVED LEMON RIND a North African specialty; lemons are quartered and preserved in salt and lemon juice or water. To use, remove and discard pulp, squeeze juice from rind, rinse rind well; slice thinly. Sold in jars or singly by most delicatessens; once opened, store under refrigeration.

RED RADISH peppery root vegetable related to the mustard plant. The small round red variety is the mildest; it is crisp and juicy, and eaten raw in salads.

RHUBARB has thick, celery-like stalks that can reach up to 60cm long (choose fresh crisp stalks); the stalks are the only edible portion of the plant, as the leaves contain a toxic substance.

RICE

arborio small, round-grain rice suited to absorb a large amount of liquid.

basmati a white, fragrant long-grained rice. Wash several times before cooking.

brown retains the outer bran layer of the rice grain. When cooked, it has a slightly chewy texture and a delicate nut-like flavour.

medium-grain a versatile rice, such as calrose, that can be substituted for short- or long-grain rices if necessary.

jasmine fragrant long-grained rice; white rice can be substituted, but will not taste the same.

ROLLED OATS oat groats (which are oats that have been husked) that have been steamed-softened, flattened with rollers, dried and then packaged.

SAUCE

chilli we use a hot variety made from thai red chillies, salt and vinegar. Use sparingly, increasing the quantity to suit your taste.

fish also called nam pla or nuoc nam; made from pulverised salted fermented fish (most often anchovies). It has a pungent smell and a strong taste. There are many versions of varying intensity, so use according to your taste.

oyster Asian in origin, this rich, brown sauce is made from oysters and their brine, cooked with salt and soy sauce, and thickened with starches.

plum a thick, sweet and sour sauce made from plums, vinegar, sugar, chillies and spices.

soy made from fermented soya beans. Several variations are available in most supermarkets and Asian food stores. We use a mild Japanese-style variety in our recipes; possibly the best table soy and the one to choose if you only want to use one variety. *Light soy* is fairly thin in consistency and, while paler than the others, is the saltiest tasting; used in dishes in which the natural colour of the ingredients is to be maintained. Not to be confused with salt-reduced or low-sodium soy sauces.

sweet chilli a mild, thai-style sauce made from red chillies, sugar, garlic and vinegar.

tamari similar to, but thicker than, japanese soy sauce; very dark in colour with a distinctively mellow flavour.

tomato also known as ketchup or catsup; a flavoured condiment made from tomatoes, vinegar and spices.

worcestershire this dark brown spicy condiment is made from soy sauce, garlic, tamarind, onions, molasses, lime, anchovies, vinegar and other seasonings. Is available in supermarkets.

SUGAR

brown a finely granulated, extremely soft sugar retaining molasses for its characteristic colour and flavour.

caster also known as superfine or finely granulated table sugar.

palm also known as nam tan pip, jawa, jaggery or gula melaka; made from the sap of the sugar palm tree. Light brown to black in colour and usually sold in rock-hard cakes. If palm sugar is unavailable, substitute with brown sugar, instead.

white a coarse, granulated sugar, also known as crystal or table sugar.

SULTANAS dried grapes, also known as golden raisins.

SUMAC a purple-red, astringent spice ground from berries growing on wild shrubs around the Mediterranean; has a tart, lemony flavour.

SUNFLOWER KERNELS dried husked sunflower seeds.

TOFU also known as bean curd, is an off-white, custard-like product made from the 'milk' of crushed soya beans; comes fresh as soft or firm. Leftover fresh tofu can be refrigerated in water (changed daily) up to four days.

firm made by compressing tofu to remove most of the water. Good for stir-fries as it can be tossed without falling apart.

silken refers to the method by which it is made – where it is strained through a silken cloth.

TOMATO

cherry also known as tiny tim or tom thumb tomatoes, small and round.

grape are about the size of a grape; they can be oblong, pear or grape-shaped and are often used whole in salads or eaten as a snack.

paste triple-concentrated tomato puree.

roma also called egg or plum; these are the smallish, oval-shaped tomatoes used in Italian cooking.

semi-dried partially dried tomato pieces in olive oil; softer and juicier than sun-dried, these are not a preserve so do not keep as long as sun-dried tomatoes.

sun-dried preserved sun-dried tomatoes.

VANILLA EXTRACT made by pulping chopped vanilla beans with a mixture of alcohol and water. A strong solution, so only a couple of drops are needed.

VINEGAR

balsamic made from the juice of trebbiano grapes; it is a deep rich brown colour with a sweet and sour flavour. Originally from Modena, Italy, there are now many balsamic vinegars on the market ranging in pungency and quality, depending on how long they have been aged. Quality can be determined up to a point by price; use the most expensive sparingly.

brown malt made from fermented malt and beech shavings.

cider (apple cider) made from crushed fermented apples.

red wine based on a blend of fermented red wine.

rice a colourless vinegar made from fermented rice and flavoured with sugar and salt. Also known as seasoned rice vinegar.

white wine made from a blend of white wines.

WASABI available as a paste in tubes or powdered in tins from Asian food stores and some supermarkets. Used to make the pungent, green-coloured sauce traditionally served with Japanese raw fish dishes.

WATERCRESS also known as winter rocket. Is one of the cress family, a large group of peppery greens used raw in salads, dips and sandwiches, or cooked in soups. Highly perishable, so must be used as soon as possible after purchase.

WOMBOK also known as napa, peking or chinese cabbage or petsai. Elongated in shape with pale green, crinkly leaves, this is the most common cabbage used in South-East Asian cooking; it can be shredded or chopped and eaten raw, or braised, steamed or stir-fried.

ZA'ATAR a blend of whole roasted sesame seeds, sumac and crushed dried herbs such as wild marjoram and thyme; its content is largely determined by the individual maker. Available in delicatessens, specialty food stores and some supermarkets.

INDEX

This book is published in 2015 by Octopus Publishing Group Limited
based on materials licensed to it by Bauer Media Books, Australia

Bauer Media Books is a division of Bauer Media Pty Limited.

54 Park St, Sydney; GPO Box 4088, Sydney, NSW 2001, Australia

phone (+61) 2 9282 8618; fax (+61) 2 9126 3702

www.awwcookbooks.com.au

MEDIA GROUP

BAUER MEDIA BOOKS

Publisher – Jo Runciman

Editorial & food director – Pamela Clark

Director of sales, marketing & rights – Brian Cearnes

Creative director – Hieu Chi Nguyen

Art director – Hannah Blackmore

Senior editor – Wendy Bryant

Food editor – Emma Braz

Published and Distributed in the United Kingdom by Octopus Publishing Group

Endeavour House

189 Shaftesbury Avenue

London WC2H 8JY

phone (+44) (0) 207 632 5400; fax (+44) (0) 207 632 5405

info@octopus-publishing.co.uk;

www.octopusbooks.co.uk

Printed by Toppan Printing Co., Hong Kong.

International foreign language rights, Brian Cearnes, Bauer Media Books bcearnes@bauer-media.com.au

A catalogue record for this book is available from the British Library.
ISBN: 978 1909770 195 (paperback)

THE AUSTRALIAN Women's Weekly

ALSO FROM THE BEST-SELLING COOKERY SERIES OF ALL TIME

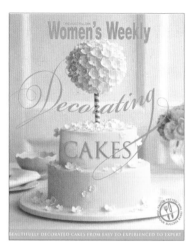

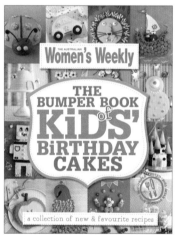

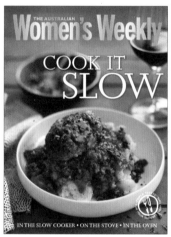

To order books visit www.octopusbooks.co.uk or telephone +44 (0)1903 828 503